BIP
10-15-93

Francis Bacon

PRAEGER PATHFINDER BIOGRAPHIES

MARTIN LUTHER
Leader of the Reformation
by Leonard W. Cowie

ARISTOTLE
Founder of Scientific Philosophy
by Benjamin Farrington

MARIE CURIE
Pioneer of the Atomic Age
by Alan Ivimey

CHARLES DARWIN
Pioneer in the Theory of Evolution
by H. E. L. Mellersh

MOHAMMED
Prophet of the Religion of Islam
by E. Royston Pike

Francis Bacon

PIONEER OF PLANNED SCIENCE

BENJAMIN FARRINGTON

FREDERICK A. PRAEGER, *Publishers*
New York • Washington

BOOKS THAT MATTER

Published in the United States of America in 1969
by Frederick A. Praeger, Inc., Publishers
111 Fourth Avenue, New York, N.Y. 10003

Library of Congress Catalog Card Number: 74–86512

Printed in the United States of America

Contents

List of Illustrations

Francis Bacon

Certainly it is heaven upon earth to have a man's mind move in charity, rest in providence, and turn upon the poles of truth.

—FRANCIS BACON, in "Of Truth"

Introduction

The life of Francis Bacon spanned the reigns of Elizabeth I and James I. What Englishmen did at this period not only made their country great but constitutes an epoch in the history of the world. Its greatest literary expression is Shakespeare. But, if another figure is to stand by his, it must be Francis Bacon. His *Essays*, his *Advancement of Learning*, his *Great Instauration*, his *New Atlantis*, and his *History of the Reign of Henry VII* are so many masterpieces.

But it is not as a literary force that Bacon is supreme. His life, whether as a writer, a member of Parliament, Lord Chancellor, or a philosopher, was dominated by the dream of effecting an alteration in the conditions of human life on earth. He sought to accomplish this by the application of science to the control of the material environment. It is this that is known as the Baconian philosophy, and it is easy to see how much has been done in the four hundred years since he was born to rid the world, along lines suggested by him, of poverty, disease, and ignorance, and how desirable it is to press on with the work at all possible speed.

His philosophy, however, understood in this sense, gives too narrow a view of the greatness of the man. Francis Bacon did not think that science could be wisely applied to the relief of man's estate except in a certain religious, political, moral, and cultural context. One and the same wisdom guided him in his career as author, member of Parliament, holder of office, or solitary student of science. Here we shall examine him in the round, for it is his all-around wisdom that entitles him, if anything does, to be called "the man who drafted the program of the modern world." He sought to set before science a new goal, the relief of man's estate; he was well aware that this meant endowing society with not only a new mind but a new conscience as well.

I

Boyhood

Not many stories are told about Francis Bacon as a boy. The little we do hear suggests that he was both precocious and engaging. He was the youngest of the eight children of Sir Nicholas Bacon, Lord Keeper of the Great Seal of England. This meant that he was often about the Court, and, when Queen Elizabeth took notice of him and asked his age, he delighted her with his reply: "Two years younger than your Majesty's happy reign." She used, we are told, to try him with questions. She must have been impressed by his answers, as she took to calling him her "young Lord Keeper."

When the question of his going to the university arose, the Queen had her say in this matter also. His elder brother Anthony had reached the age of fourteen, a normal age for a Cambridge student in those days. But Anthony and Francis were close friends, Francis was very forward for his years, and there was much to be said for their going together. The question was whether Francis knew enough Latin. Elizabeth herself tested him, and he passed the examination with distinction. Next April, the brothers went to Cambridge together, Francis being about twelve years and three months old.

In London, Sir Nicholas, the Lord Keeper, lived at York House in the Strand. The Strand then deserved its name. York House commanded an uninterrupted view of the Thames across its own well-ordered grounds. The short journey to the royal palace of Whitehall could be made by boat or through green fields. It was natural that the young Francis should sometimes accompany his father to the Court. He had other family connections with it. Only one of the Queen's ministers had greater influence than Sir Nicholas, but he was Francis's uncle, Lord Burghley, the Lord High Treasurer. Sir Nicholas and Lord Burghley were married to sisters; Lady Burghley was Francis's aunt Mildred. Such connections indicated a political career for Francis, if he should prove fit.

Such evidence as we have shows the home at York House to have been a happy one. Of the eight children, six—three boys and three girls—were by an earlier marriage. Anthony and Francis were the sons of the second wife—Anne Cooke, Mildred's sister. Mildred and Anne had inherited considerable intelligence from their father, Sir Anthony Cooke, who had been tutor to Edward VI. Mildred is said to have known Latin, Greek, and Hebrew. Anne knew no Hebrew, but she won a place for herself in the history of the English Church by her translation from the Latin of Bishop Jewel's *Defence* of it. When Parker, the Archbishop of Canterbury, saw her English version, he thought so well of it that he had it printed as soon as possible, and it is, indeed, a model of the translator's art.

Not surprisingly, then, Anne's two sons, Anthony and

Francis, outshone their older half-brothers and -sisters, and, of the two, Francis enjoyed better health and had the brighter mind. So it came about that, of all his children, Sir Nicholas built his highest hopes on the youngest. This, no doubt, Elizabeth understood when she called him her "young Lord Keeper." He was the one best fitted to succeed his able father.

Sir Nicholas, then, to the end of his days, had good grounds for the excellent spirits with which history credits him. His second wife had not only given him two clever sons; she also looked after him well and was able to give him intellectual companionship. Some verses survive in which Sir Nicholas—who, it must be admitted, was no great poet—praises her for the skill and care with which she nursed him through a long illness, for her cheerfulness, and for the entertainment she gave him by reading aloud from their favorite authors. One would never guess who these were, unless he remembered that the English novel had not yet been born. Sir Nicholas's fancy was for Seneca, and his wife's for Cicero. I suppose she read them in the original Latin.

Nor was she only a good wife; she was a good mother too. Long after her husband's death she continued to write fidgety, affectionate letters to her sons. She decayed in mind and temper as she aged. But, when she died in 1610, Francis, then forty-nine years old, felt her loss deeply. Anthony had already been dead some years, but we possess a letter written by Francis to a close friend, Sir Michael Hicks, in which he begs him to give him his company for a few days to help him "pass over this mournful occasion with more comfort." This letter suggests, what all we know about him confirms, that an affectionate home life had produced in Francis its usual effect, the capacity for making and keeping friends.

Francis had another home besides York House, to which

he was bound by the happiest memories. When he was about three, his father began to build for himself (he was a great builder) a new house at Gorhambury, near St. Albans. The house took three or four years to build, and Francis, who had the gift of learning by direct observation as much as through books, must have been familiar with all the trades involved— those of the sawyers, carpenters, masons, bricklayers, joiners, plasterers, glaziers, quarrymen, pavers, and plumbers. He always remembered how every room in the house was supplied with water piped from ponds about a mile off. He remembered, too, the picture his father had had painted and placed over the fireplace in the dining hall, which showed Ceres introducing to the famished race of men the art of grain-growing. This was the symbol of the Agricultural Revolution, the first great technical revolution, which transformed the conditions of human life. It was for Francis a sort of model and precedent of the next great technical revolution, the Industrial Revolution, of which he made himself the eloquent prophet.

Queen Elizabeth came twice to stay as a visitor in this house —once in 1572, when Francis, who was then eleven, was no doubt there, and again in 1577, when Francis was away in France. On the death of Sir Nicholas, the property passed to Anthony, and Lady Anne went to reside there. When Anthony died, he left it to Francis. How deeply Francis loved the house and how intimately it was bound up with his memories of his father are indicated by a strange incident recorded by him in old age: When he was eighteen years of age and away in Paris with the English Ambassador, "I had," he records, "a dream, which I told to divers English gentlemen, that my father's house in the country was plastered all over with black mortar." This sinister dream was followed in a few

days by the news of his father's sudden death. Such phenomena of the imagination seem to arise between close rela-
tives, Bacon suggests. He classes the incident among the "many
reports in history that upon the death of persons of such
nearness men have an inward feeling of it."

But we are anticipating events in speaking of the death of
Sir Nicholas, and we must now return to the boy of twelve
who had just left home for the first time, to go and study
at Cambridge.

2

Cambridge and Paris

The chief requirement for matriculation as a university student at this time was the ability to read and write Latin. This was taught at the grammar school, and this, I suppose, Francis had acquired at home from his tutors, with some help from his mother and father. At the university, however, the basis of study was no longer Latin grammar but logic. Grammar had taught the rules of correct expression, and Francis had taken to this like a duck to water. Logic claimed to teach the rules of correct thinking. Francis worked hard at the various exercises traditionally supposed to produce this result. But, although he was only fourteen when his university career came to an end, he had by that time come to see that the system was more an obstacle than an aid to the acquisition of knowledge. The rest of his life was devoted to expressing this point of view.

This revolt of a boy in his teens against a traditional system of education is a very remarkable occurrence, not because of the revolt but because he was right.

The training given at the universities at this time was poor in both content and method. The information consisted of collections of established opinions on the various branches of knowledge derived from the schools of ancient Greece; the student showed his mastery of what he had learned by defending the truth of some received opinion against criticism by others. The subjects covered were metaphysics, physics (that is, natural philosophy), ethics, and politics. It had been the ambition of the Greeks to present every branch of knowledge as a closely knit logical system deduced from the smallest possible number of axioms, or first principles. In this, their model had been geometry, but the method has the disadvantage of making a science seem to depend altogether on reason and not at all on observation. The unsuitability of the method was most obvious in the natural sciences. Nothing was done to suggest that science is a body of knowledge that grows, not simply by thinking but by experimenting as well. Nothing was done, either, to show how scientific knowledge can be applied in practice. Truth was established by argument, not by seeing if it worked.

The logical structure of ancient science had developed slowly. The great systematizer of logic had been Aristotle, and the whole encyclopedia of the Greek sciences had descended to the modern world unified and coordinated on his principles. Nor was it only the pagan philosophy of ancient Greece that was presented in this way. In the later Middle Ages, Aristotelian logic had been applied to the new task of organizing Christian dogma into a vast theological system. Over the whole field of knowledge, both religious and secular, the influence of Aristotle reigned supreme.

Now Francis Bacon was far from being the first to quarrel with this system of education and this way of thought. In the religious field as early as the time of Henry VIII, English humanists, like Colet and Thomas More and their Dutch friend Erasmus, had protested at the way in which, under the scholastic system of philosophy, Aristotle had been allowed to dominate all thought. Francis Bacon had been brought up to sympathize with this revolt. Furthermore, in the secular field, there were some, including Sir Nicholas Bacon, who had begun to feel that the sciences, taught in the Aristotelian way that was fashionable in the universities, had little or no bearing on the industrial developments characteristic of the age.

It is plain that there was much in his background, even in his home influences, to make Francis Bacon critical of the type of education he was receiving at Cambridge. Nevertheless, there remains something quite startling in the clarity with which, at so young an age, he defined the defect in the system, and in the determination with which he set himself to correct it. It proved to be the main task of his life, but he was only fourteen when he came to understand it. We have his own word for this, although, not unnaturally, he got the dates a little confused. For he was quite an old man when he told his chaplain, and biographer, Dr. Rawley, what he remembered about it.

This is Dr. Rawley's report: "Whilst he was commorant [that is, resident] in the university, about sixteen years of age, as his lordship hath been pleased to report unto myself, he first fell into the dislike of the philosophy of Aristotle; not for the worthlessness of the author, to whom he would ever ascribe all high attributes, but for the unfruitfulness of the way; being a philosophy (as his lordship used to say) only strong for disputations and contentions, but barren of the production of works for the benefit of the life of man; in which mind he continued to his dying day."

The statement is so simple that it is easy to miss how momentous it is. Through it, we see straight into the mind of the boy and into what continued to be the mind of the man throughout his life. And what we see is not only an intellectual but also a moral judgment. Francis Bacon has been sent to Cambridge as the first step to a political career, and he revolts from what he is being taught, not at all because it will not further his personal interests but because he judges it not to be in the interests of the human race. That he had a great and original mind no one has ever doubted; the originality and force of his conscience have not so often been understood. But by what other name are we to call the burning vision that accompanied him throughout life—the vision of a new kind of society that neither suffered the resources of nature to lie waste nor exploited them for selfish ends but recognized the sacred obligation to apply them to the relief of man's estate?

Francis left the university in December, 1575, and, the following June, Anthony and he were entered as students at Gray's Inn in London, because the study of law was the next stage of preparation for a political career. But, three months later, he was accorded a more significant privilege. His father secured for him a place in the retinue of Sir Amyas Paulet, who was about to retire as English Ambassador to the French Court. In September, Francis landed at Calais, not to return (except possibly as a special messenger to the Queen) until March, 1579.

Thus, Francis had two and a half years in France, and there is much evidence that he was deeply impressed by the mismanaged affairs of that kingdom in contrast with the England of Elizabeth, where the influence of his own father and uncle counted for so much. His residence in France began only a few years after the hideous massacre of St. Bartholomew, to which in his writings he more than once refers. He was impressed by the unhappy division of the kingdom in matters of religion and of state; by the degradation of justice owing to the sale of judgeships; by the waste of the treasury, the overtaxing of the people, and the ruin of the countryside—wrongs which had already bred great trouble and were likely to breed more. Such were the evils he sought to avoid for his own country, if, as was not unlikely, he should ever come to power.

But on his return home he found his personal fortunes had taken an unfavorable turn. Not only was his father dead, but, dying suddenly, he had been unable to make provision for the youngest and, one must believe, the best loved of his sons. Anthony inherited Gorhambury, but there was nothing for Francis. It is a monument to the friendship between the brothers, to the generosity of Anthony, and to the improvidence of Francis that he was never afterward out of his brother's debt.

3

Gray's Inn and the Study of the Law

Francis, it will be remembered, had already been admitted to Gray's Inn before he went to Paris, and to it he returned when his father's death brought him back to England. In age, Francis had been no more than a schoolboy when he went to Cambridge; but the law students, who entered on their courses at seventeen or eighteen and might stay six or eight years at their studies, were more like modern university students. The Inns of Court, in fact, consisting of Gray's Inn, Lincoln's Inn, the Middle Temple, and the Inner Temple, together with the nine Inns of Chancery, were London's great legal university. The right of residence might, in certain instances, be retained after training was complete. Francis was popular at his Inn and filled many offices of trust. He was successively Dean of the Chapel, Lent Reader, and Treasurer; and he continued to hold his chambers in the Inn to the end of his life.

In such a place as this, a friendly man might hope to make worthwhile friends. The friend of Bacon's choice was a Mr. Bettenham. His memory is embalmed in two of his sayings, which Bacon included in his collection of *Apophthegms*. "Mr. Bettenham," Bacon records, "used to say that riches were like muck; when it lay upon an heap, it gave but a stench and ill odour; but when it was spread upon the ground, then it was the cause of much fruit." This sentiment determined Bacon's course of action all his life. The other entry runs: "The same Mr. Bettenham said, that virtuous men were like some herbs and spices, that gave not their sweet smell, till they be broken and crushed." It fell to Bacon's lot to commemorate his friend. He erected an arbor to his memory in the grounds of Gray's Inn, and did not fail to surround it with a carpet of such wild herbs as would yield a sweet scent when trodden under foot.

Anthony and Francis were together at Gray's Inn as they had been at Cambridge. Their mother's letters, addressed to the elder brother but intended for both, show that if it was possible to work too hard at the Inn it was also possible to have some diversions. We have a letter of hers dated in 1592, when Francis was thirty-one.

"I verily think," she writes, "your brother's weak stomach to digest hath been much caused and confirmed by untimely going to bed and then musing *nescio quid* when he should be alseep." What she meant by *nescio quid* ("some nonsense or other") we shall see in a moment. Meanwhile, here is another quotation, this from a letter of 1594: "I trust they will not mum nor mask nor sinfully revel at Gray's Inn." In fact, in Elizabethan times, theatricals were quite a feature of life in the Inn. For such dangers the staunch old puritan had her favorite remedy. "I trust you, with your servants, use prayer twice in a day, having been where reformation is" (Anthony had resided in Geneva). "Omit it not for any. Your brother is too negligent therein."

Francis, whether or not he satisfied his mother in the matter of his prayers, was interested in theatricals. But characteristically he turned them to his own ends, and it is what survives of his contributions to one or two of these entertainments that reveals what the *nescio quid*, the bee in his bonnet, was that kept him up late and prevented his going to sleep. It was nothing else than the vision he had had as a boy at Cambridge of a world transformed by science in the service of man. We know this because he twice seized the opportunity of theatrical entertainments presented at Gray's Inn in honor of the Queen, to draw her attention to the possibilities of this reform.

At one of these entertainments, a "device" organized by the earl of Essex for the Queen's birthday in 1592, there was recited a piece called *Mr Bacon in praise of Learning*. A few sentences from it will reveal the very definite shape his vision had now assumed in his mind:

"Are we richer by one poor invention by reason of all the learning that hath been these many hundred years? The industry of artificers maketh some small improvement of things invented; and chance sometimes in experimenting maketh us to stumble upon somewhat new; but all the disputation of the learned never brought to light one effect of nature before unknown.

"All the philosophy of nature which is now received is either the philosophy of the Grecians or that of the alchemists. That of the Grecians hath the foundations in words, in ostentation, in confutation, in sects, in schools, in disputations. That of the alchemists hath the foundation in imposture, in auricular [i.e., handed down by word of mouth] traditions, and obscurity. The one never faileth to multiply words, and the other ever faileth to multiply gold."

The Queen, unhappily, was not impressed. Very probably she shared the view of Bacon's mother that he had a bee in his bonnet. But the project as he conceived it was so vast, that it needed the royal support; it needed to become part of public policy. Accordingly, Bacon returned to the attack at the first opportunity. This was provided by the presentation of another "device" in 1594. This took more of the form of a spectacle. Six courtiers presented themselves before the prince of an imaginary realm to offer him advice on different aspects of government. Bacon wrote all six speeches. I quote only from the one in which he tried again to awaken the Queen's interest in the possibilities of the new science:

"I will wish unto your Highness the exercise of the best and purest part of the mind, and the most innocent and meriting conquest, being the conquest of the works of nature. And to this purpose I will commend to your Highness four principal works and monuments of yourself. First the collecting of a most perfect and general library, wherein whatever the wit of man hath heretofore committed to books of worth, be they ancient or modern, printed or manuscript, European or of other parts, of one or other language, may be made contributory to your wisdom.

"Next, a spacious, wonderful garden, wherein whatsoever plant the sun of divers climates, out of the earth of divers moulds, either wild or by the culture of man brought forth, may be with that care that appertaineth to the good prospering thereof set and cherished: this garden to be built about with room to stable in all rare beasts and to cage in all rare birds; with two lakes adjoining, the one of fresh water the other of salt, for like variety of fishes. And so you may have in small compass a model of universal nature made private.

"The third, a goodly huge cabinet, wherein whatsoever the hand of man by exquisite art or engine hath made rare in stuff, form, or motion; whatsoever singularity change and the shuffle of things hath produced; whatsoever nature hath wrought in things that want life and may be kept; shall be sorted and included.

"The fourth, such a still-house, so furnished with mills, instruments, furnaces and vessels, as may be a place fit for a philosopher's stone."

The Queen still showed no interest, but Bacon continued throughout life to elaborate his project until it reached the fullest expression he was able to give it in his chief master-piece, *The Great Instauration*, that is, the fresh start, the new beginning. The publication of this, however, was delayed till his own elevation to the position of Lord Chancellor in 1620. That is a subject we will keep for a later chapter.

Meanwhile, we must remember that Bacon had also his legal studies to pursue. These studies were not only a prepara-tion for making his living. They were essential for the scien-tific reform to which his life was devoted. Without them he could not hope for a position of influence in government which he thought necessary for the furtherance of his plans. Nor was this all. Bacon never thought of science in the abstract, but concretely as it affected the lives of men. The more he pondered his project the more clearly he saw that science could flourish, and had in the past flourished, only in a society suited to it. Only in certain religious, political, and cultural conditions could science be developed and, when developed, applied to wholesome purposes. For this reason

Bacon has sometimes been called the Statesman of Science; and for statesmanship there was no school like the law.

Moreover, this was a period when the study of law was immensely stimulating intellectually. It opened the door to one of the greatest explorations undertaken in the Elizabethan age—the exploration not of foreign lands, but of the past of England herself. Without this exploration England could never have attained that deepening of the national consciousness which is one of the chief features of the age, and one which Bacon not only shared but helped to create. An example will best explain how legal studies contributed to this end.

Sir Henry Spelman (1564–1641), almost an exact contemporary of Francis Bacon, went, like him, to Trinity, Cambridge, and then entered at one of the Inns of Court— Lincoln's Inn. At a period when so much church land was being converted to lay uses, he interested himself particularly in the history of ecclesiastical properties. When and under what circumstances had these ecclesiastical properties arisen? Was their transference to lay owners always justifiable? Engrossed in such questions, he discovered the uncertainty attached to the meaning of both Anglo-Saxon and Roman legal terminology. He began to compile a *Glossary* of legal terms, and lent a hand in the setting up of a lectureship in Anglo-Saxon at Cambridge, which in its turn contributed to the making of the first Saxon dictionary.

To fix the meaning of legal terms is not only of linguistic interest. When the meaning of the term has been found, it brings to light the hidden history of the institutions of the past. One of the disputed words, for instance, was the late Latin term *feudum*. It is from this word the feudal system gets its name. In order to establish his interpretation of the term, Spelman executed a fine piece of research into *The Original Growth, Propagation and Condition of Tenures by*

Knight Service. In it he laid bare for the first time the fundamental institutions of feudalism.

The solution of one problem suggests another. In that Bible-reading age, the nature of Jewish law was a matter of great curiosity. Spelman extended his researches and produced the most voluminous of his works. It was called *Concerning Law Terms, wherein the Laws of the Jews, Grecians, Romans, Saxons, and Normans are fully explained.* One can see at a glance the contribution made by legal studies to the maturing self-consciousness of the English people. What was found out about the Normans and the Saxons was the key to their own past. What was said about the Jews, Greeks, and Romans set the new civilization of England in relation with the three great civilized peoples of antiquity whose thought lay at the foundations of European culture.

Bacon did not specialize in these studies, but they constitute the background against which his mind took shape. All his life he was engaged in the effort to lay a solid foundation for the future greatness of his country, in which he firmly believed and to which he aspired to contribute. He realized that the England of his day was a new creation, and he had the idea that the new England could best be understood in the light of what happened between 1485 and 1603, that is, to use a phrase of his own, in the period "from the union of the Roses to the union of the Crowns." He indicated the need for such a history at quite an early period in his career; and in the first six months of leisure after his dramatic fall from power he executed a considerable part of it in his *Reign of Henry VII.*

He was also intensely aware of the role played by a good system of laws in the maintenance of internal peace. In 1596, two years after the second of his theatrical "devices" at Gray's Inn, he attempted a different approach to the Queen. He dedicated "to Her Sacred Majesty" a little treatise called *Maxims of the Law*. In it he speaks of law-making as "a fruit of Peace" and compliments the Queen on her successful avoidance of war. "The most excellent princes," he writes, "have ever studied to adorn and honour times of peace with the amendment of the policy of their laws." He then speaks with admiration of the civil law of Rome, noting that its excellency was such that France, Italy, and Spain, though Roman domination had long passed away, still continued to use the policy of that law. But he was aware of the very different history of English law, resting, as it does, not on a code but on custom. He holds himself, he says, "a debtor to my profession," and would like to repay the debt by improving the laws. Hence his endeavor to draw from the mass of precedents the general maxims of the law. In this endeavor he aids himself by noting where the civil law of Rome and the customary law of England concur, diverge, or contradict one another.

Finally, he gives a certain urgency to the undertaking by pointing out to the Queen, with special reference to the changing circumstances of her own reign, that "times of peace, drawing for the most part with them abundance of wealth and fineness of cunning, do draw also, in further consequence, multitude of suits and controversies, and abuses of law by evasion and devices; which inconveniences in such times growing more general, do more instantly solicit for the amendment of the laws to restrain and repress them."

It is as if he wished to let the Queen know that, quite apart from the scientific bee in his bonnet, he had other capacities also which she might be glad to employ. And this was true. There was a statesman in Francis Bacon as well as a philosopher of science.

4

In Parliament

We have been discussing Bacon's ideas of philosophical and legal reform, and we left him in our last chapter in 1596, at the age of thirty-five, still busy with his legal studies at Gray's Inn. What we have failed so far to mention is that by this time he was also a seasoned parliamentarian, having been a member of the House of Commons for some twelve years. He first entered parliament in 1584 as the member from Melcome Regis. In subsequent parliaments he represented Taunton, Middlesex, Ipswich, St. Albans, and Cambridge. Sometimes he was chosen by two constituencies, once by three.

In Parliament, he was noted for the independence of his views; he was admired and feared for his eloquence; he was popular and respected. But he did not acquire the position of a great party leader. Perhaps he lacked the robustness, vigor, and drive required for such a role; or, more simply, perhaps he lacked the will. Often in later life he deplored the amount of time and energy he had given to politics. Then he used to say, with the Psalmist, that his soul had been a stranger in it. Or, using an image from the Gospel, he would regret that he had wasted his talent, meaning that if he had stuck to his scientific reform he would have acted more in accordance with the role of benefactor of mankind which in his heart of hearts he believed Providence had assigned him.

But his sense of frustration in politics must not be allowed to obscure the great part he did play. He lived in the generation before the Civil War and foresaw the disastrous cleavage between Crown and Commons; and, though he had not the power to make his views prevail, those views were so sound that some authorities believe that, if they had prevailed, they would have sufficed to avert the bloody interlude of the revolution.

The main source of friction between the Crown and the Commons was the question of finance, and Bacon had formed his ideas of the right way to handle this difficult matter in the more generous, large, and spacious climate of Queen Elizabeth's reign. But by no amount of tact or plain speaking could he bring James I to act in the same spirit. This is a question that demands a little space.

First we might consider his ideal of what the House of Commons should be. He was absolutely against the notion of a packed house. Only an assembly of independent, intelligent, and experienced men could shoulder the responsibilities he would lay upon it. "I wish by all means," he writes to King James, "that the house may be compounded, not of young men, but of the greatest gentlemen of quality of their country, and ancient parliament men, and the principal and gravest lawyers . . . and the chiefest merchants, and likewise travellers and statesmen; and, in a word, that it be a sufficient house, worthy to consult within the great causes of the commonwealth."

In the spirit of this ideal he had acted under Elizabeth. In the parliament of 1593, when Bacon was anxiously courting the favor of the Queen, a proposal for a large subsidy earnestly desired by her was under discussion. Bacon was not averse to seeking ways and means by which the country's needs might be met and the money found, but of the actual proposals made he uttered a scathing criticism. He thought them oppressive and therefore likely to prove ineffective. "The poor men's rent," he said, "is such as they are not able to yield it. The gentlemen must sell their plate and the farmers their brass pots ere this will be paid. And as for us"—and here he voiced what always remained his opinion of the duties of the house—"as for us, we are here to search the wounds of the realm, not to skin them over; wherefore we are not to persuade ourselves of their wealth more than it is."

The words were reported to the Queen, and they must have stung her. After all, neither such racy eloquence nor such sympathy for the poor nor such a keen sense of the duty of a representative of the people, were foreign to her character. She found it hard to forgive the man she had once called her "young Lord Keeper." For some years he was denied the right of access to her presence. But in the depths of her nature she was the same sort of person as he was.

This was shown on another occasion when the Commons indicated their disapproval of a long list of concessions for which she had asked. She revoked the lot of her own accord, and when the Commons sent a deputation to thank her she spoke first of their love and loyalty to their Sovereign. Then she went on: "Of myself I must say this; I was never any greedy,

Francis Bacon as Lord Chancellor

Francis Bacon, age twelve, from a life-size terra cotta bust

Lady Anne Bacon, mother of Francis, by the same sculptor. These two busts were done at about the same time.

scraping grasper, nor a strait fast-holding Prince, not yet a waster. My heart was never set on worldly goods, but only for my subjects' good. What you do bestow on me I will not hoard it up, but receive it to bestow on you again. Yea, mine own properties I count yours, to be expended for your good. Therefore render unto them [that is, the members of the House] from me, I beseach you, Mr. Speaker, such thanks as you imagine my heart yieldeth but my tongue cannot express."

Such a speech set the standard for Bacon of what a prince should be in relation to the representatives of the people. But when, in the new reign, he found James stooping to devious tricks to get money out of the Commons, he was stricken with dismay. He wrote to him with a frankness Elizabeth might have resented but would have understood, but which James neither understood nor resented, to urge "that your Majesty do for this parliament put off the person of a merchant or contractor, and rest upon the person of a King."

It was Bacon's cousin, Robert Cecil, now Lord Treasurer, who was misleading the King. But Bacon, remembering Elizabeth's queenly words: "What you do bestow on me I will not hoard it up, but receive it to bestow on you again," wrote to James to lament that England, under Cecil's schemes, should "be like the land of Egypt watered by certain streams and cuts of his own devising" and "should be no more like the Land of Promise watered with the dew of heaven, which sometimes was drawn from the earth and sometimes fell back upon the earth again." The quality of such eloquence, whether uttered in the house or submitted to the King in a private advice, springs from a moral sensibility of rare quality. The wisdom of Bacon was drawn from the depths of his moral as well as his rational being; and like the Biblical writers, his thought, when perfected, expressed itself in images. One thinks of the last words of King David: "He that ruleth over men must be just, ruling in the fear of God. And he shall be as the light of the morning, when the sun riseth, even a morning without clouds; as the tender grass springing out of the earth by clear shining after rain."

Bacon, we see, had thought deeply about the relation of the King and the Commons. His thought did not stop there, but extended to every class in the community. In his speech on the subsidy, he had shown as much concern for the poor and the farmers as for the gentlemen. England was undergoing rapid change at this time. A word or two on his attitude to the chief problems may fittingly conclude this chapter.

One such problem concerned the enclosure of new lands, the process, which was beginning to develop pace at this time, by which most of the land ceased to be common and became private. Bacon was not against enclosures. He knew that many who were enclosing lands were putting them to better use. The "inning" of land, as he called the bringing of waste land under cultivation, had his warm support. But to take good arable land from yeomen and turn it into pasture was good neither for agriculture nor for the military strength of the country. It decreased wealth, reduced man power, and in particular depleted the yeomanry who were the backbone of the army. With scorn, Bacon had noted how the French, by sacrificing their peasantry to the nobility, had thrown away the power to fight. For while a numerous nobility meant a magnificent cavalry, it was the infantry, the yeomen, who won battles.

Accordingly, in the Parliament of 1597, Bacon proposed that "all lands turned into pasture since the Queen's accession, no less a period than forty years, should be taken from the deer and sheep within eighteen months and restored to the yeomen and the plough." In 1601, he raised the same point again: "It stands not with the policy of the State that the wealth of the kingdom should be engrossed into a few pasturers' hands." It was in consideration of such policies that the historian S. R. Gardiner said: "To carry out his programme would have been to avert the evils of the next half-century. . . . He was the one man capable of preventing a catastrophe by anticipating the demands of the age." And to this we must add that his scientific project was directed to precisely the same ends.

It should surprise nobody to learn that it was in 1584, the year he entered Parliament, that Bacon committed to paper his first attempt at a systematic statement of his plan. He made his debut as the propounder of a new philosophy and as a parliamentarian simultaneously. The fact is significant. His philosophy and his politics were two aspects of the one endeavor—the health, wealth, and well-being of his country.

5

The Greatest Birth of Time

The philosophical work Bacon wrote about the time he first entered Parliament was in Latin, the learned language of the day. Parliament was full of university men, and he intended his essay for private circulation only. It was called *Temporis Partus Maximus*, that is, *The Greatest Birth of Time*. Forty years later, we find him smiling at the youthful self-confidence that enabled him to give it such a boastful title. But he does not disown the contents. He makes it quite clear that the writing was simply an early exposition of the philosophy to which, in his old age, he remained committed.

Nor was the title as boastful as it might seem. It has in fact turned out to be true that the application of science to technique has made such a change in human destiny as may fairly be called the greatest birth of time. Nevertheless, Bacon came to dislike the phrase; and, when he rehandled the same theme at a later period, he modified the title in a subtle way. This later work, which we shall discuss in another chapter, he called *Temporis Partus Masculus*, or *The Male Birth of Time*. If we recall the old saying, Truth is the *daughter* of Time, we shall get the point of the new title. Like everyone in his age, Bacon believed in the superiority of the male. What he meant to imply was that all previous science deserved only to be called the *daughter* of Time, but with the new philosophy, Time had borne a *son*.

The earlier form of the work, that called *The Greatest Birth of Time*, has not survived. But we know what it was about, and its title makes a good heading for this chapter; for it expresses unequivocally a conviction that Bacon firmly held. He believed that an unprecedented change in human destiny was at hand. He did not, of course, think he deserved credit for the change. Neither he nor any other individual could ever have such power. What he did claim was to be able to read the signs of the times and so become the herald of the new dawn.

What were the signs that announced the passing of the ancient world and the birth of a new? We shall mention the most important.

First, there were the great voyages of exploration in which the Portuguese and the Spaniards had taken the lead, to be soon followed by the English and the Dutch. Ancient civilization, as far as Europe was concerned, had been virtually confined to the countries around the Mediterranean Sea. Transoceanic navigation changed all that. The confined stretch of water separating Europe from Africa no longer had more than a local right to be called "the Middle Sea." For the new navigators, it had become a sort of creek or inlet of the Atlantic Ocean, and the center of gravity of the inhabited world had changed. Men had now circumnavigated the globe,

and had seen with their own eyes places and peoples about
which the ancient geographers had only been able to guess.
The authority of antiquity had been profoundly shaken.
Bacon's way of putting it was that, since the map of the
physical world had been redrawn, the time had come also to
remap the intellectual world.

Connected with this enlargement of the geographical and the
intellectual horizon was another point that had begun to force
itself upon the attention of men, but which Bacon was to
make peculiarly his own by the rich development he gave it.
The success of the new distant voyages was owing in large
measure to a technical invention. It was the magnetic needle,
the mariner's compass, that had enabled men to find their path
over the trackless oceans. The ancients. when not creeping
from point to point in sight of land, navigated by the stars.
Now the compass had made man independent of the stars.
The new method of steering, then, was not to be described as
an *improvement* of the ancient art, but as a *new* art, based on
new knowledge, and ever so much more effective. This set
the standard for the new science at which Bacon aimed. Its
purpose was not to improve old arts: that could be left to the
practitioners of the various arts. Its aim was to discover new
arts, and new arts demand superior theoretical knowledge.
They are an application of science to technique.

There were other examples to enforce the same lesson.
Ancient learning had been disseminated by handwritten rolls
or books. Now the printing press had been invented. This
again was not just an improved manuscript book. Printing
was a new art. And just as the compass had revolutionized
navigation, so printing revolutionized the world of learning.
It seems improbable that a movement like the Reformation
could have taken place without it. Without it, the spread of

vernacular translations of the Bible—in the native or "home-born" languages of German, French, and English—would have been impossible. On this comparatively simple invention depended great social and cultural changes.

A third example was gunpowder. The artillery of the ancients propelled its missiles by the elastic force of twisted ropes. Over a long period of time, improvements in this method had been made, but there had been no decisive change. Then suddenly the old method was abandoned and a completely new one took its place. Men had probed deeper into the hidden forces of nature. A mysterious chemical explosion was harnessed and hurled larger missiles to vaster distances with greater accuracy than the more obvious and superficial power of twisted ropes could do.

These examples all contributed to the philosophy of invention that was maturing in Bacon's mind. If such great social effects could be produced by such comparatively simple discoveries as lay behind the compass, printing press, and gunpowder—discoveries, moreover, which seemed to have been made casually and almost by chance—what might not be achieved if men set themselves systematically to investigate the hidden forces of nature on which technical inventions rest? Might not a multiplicity of new discoveries be made with incalculable consequences for the future of mankind? Such were the thoughts that were stirring in Bacon's mind when he wrote, for circulation among his friends, his Latin essay with the boastful title of *The Greatest Birth of Time.*

Since that early work is lost, we shall quote the expression he gave to these thoughts later in life. "It is well to observe the force and effect and consequences of discoveries. These are to be seen nowhere more conspicuously than in those three which were unknown to the ancients, and of which the origin, though recent, is obscure, namely printing, gunpowder, and the magnetic needle. For these three have changed the whole face and state of things throughout the world; the first in literature, the second in warfare, the third in navigation; whence have followed innumerable changes; insomuch that no empire, no sect, no star seems to have exerted greater power and influence in human affairs than these mechanical inventions." (*Novum Organum*, 129)

And again he writes: "When I set before me the condition of these times, in which learning seems to have made her third visitation to men; and when at the same time I attentively behold the helps and assistance with which she is now provided; as the vivacity and sublimity of the many wits of this age; the noble monuments of ancient writers, which shine like so many lights before us; the art of printing, which brings books within the reach of men of all fortunes; the opened bosom of the ocean, and the world travelled over in every part, whereby multitudes of discoveries unknown to the ancients have been disclosed, and an immense mass added to natural history . . . I cannot but be raised to the hope that this period will far surpass the Greek and Roman in learning." (*De Augmentis*, VIII end)

Now it is characteristic of Bacon that these hopes did not remain with him limited to the scientific and technical sphere. In their very origin, as we have already seen, they suggested themselves as being conducive to "the benefit of the life of man," and throughout his life he always advocated them as a means to "the relief of man's estate." It is a fact that in the England of his day the problem of poverty was perpetually before Parliament; and, apart from the many practical and by no means ineffectual legislative measures that were introduced, there floated before the imagination of every educated

Englishman the intensely moving *Utopia* of Sir Thomas More. In this book the author had urged the desirability of leisure and opportunities of education for the artisans and peasants, and had even ventured to consider, if not to recommend, the remedy of an equal distribution of wealth.

It is in this context that we must understand Bacon's concern with the possibilities of science and technology. He thought of them as the best remedy for the poverty of his country and of all mankind. For this reason, when he in his turn composed his utopia, *The New Atlantis,* he imagined as its central institution a scientific and technological college under the charge of administrators for whom the care of the health and well-being of their people was a religious obligation.

The New Atlantis is an idealization of the England that Bacon hoped to assist in creating. It differs from More's *Utopia* principally in this, that More seemed able to think only in terms of a more equal distribution of existing wealth, while Bacon dreamed of the creation of an age of plenty by a transformation of the means of production. He remembered in his father's dining hall the pictures of Ceres introducing to mankind the art of agriculture. He remarked, with reference to this, that new arts are new creations, and that the Roman poet Lucretius had said of the introduction of agriculture that it *re-created* the life of primitive men. The invention of new arts was, he wrote, a sort of imitation of the work of the Creator, a means to refashioning the life of man.

So great a project could be realized only as part of government policy. For this reason he tried to interest, first the Queen, and later King James. For this reason he was no sooner in Parliament than he sought to gather around him a group of intelligent backers. For this reason it was necessary to try to discredit the Aristotelian philosophy which dominated the universities, for this philosophy had no conceivable application to the increase of production. For this reason also he attacked alchemy; for although this ancient art served as the foundation of modern chemistry, it was full of imposture and mystification and quite unfit to accomplish the task Bacon had in mind for the new science.

We must think of Bacon, then, as engaged in a war on many fronts. He is not to be compared with a scientist who has a particular line of research to which he wishes to devote his life. His intention, rather, is to change the governmental policy and the educational policy of his country to make room for a kind of research that plunged much deeper into the hidden forces of nature and sought to apply them in practice to the enrichment of his country and of mankind.

6

Command of Wits and Pens

When he was about thirty-one years of age, Bacon wrote a short autobiographical sketch (the only one he ever attempted), designed as an introduction to the philosophical work on which he was engaged. The fragment touches on his political and religious ambitions as well as his philosophical ideas. It is a very eloquent piece; but since it is written in Latin and is in any case too long to quote in full, I begin this chapter with a summary of it.

Believing himself born for the service of mankind, he considered where the need was greatest and whether he was fit to meet the need. Turning over possible careers, he reflected that the work of lawgivers and founders of states is limited to one country, while inventors and discoverers achieve something for the human race as a whole. A man who succeeded in throwing a fresh light over the whole field of nature would rightly be called "the propagator of man's dominion over the

universe, the champion of liberty, and the subduer of necessities." Bacon then turned his eyes in upon himself and made
an objective assessment of his own aptitudes. His conclusion was that his natural endowments fitted him for the
arduous career of a scientist. His duty was, therefore, to
attempt to serve all mankind rather than his own country.

But he had to remember that his family background and his
training pointed to a political career. Also, he found it hard
to justify to others his opinion that he should devote himself
to natural philosophy rather than to politics, nor could he
suppress his feeling that he owed a special duty to his own
country. Added to this was the tempting thought that an
honorable position in the State would provide him with the
necessary resources, put him in command of the necessary
"wits and pens," to carry through his program of research.
Accordingly, he compromised. He set himself to learn the
business of government, and, so far as he could without humiliation, sued for office. In this choice he was actuated also by
another motive. The arts and sciences concern only this life,
but there was also eternity to be considered. Religion was at
the time in a sorry state, and his hope was to be able to do
something also "for the good of men's souls."

This effort of self-appraisal is both candid and just. It fits
in with all that we know of Bacon's course of action. It would
have made a fine and moving introduction to a full statement
of his project. If we ask, then, why he suppressed it, or at
least never used it (for it survived among his papers to be
published after his death), the answer probably is simply
modesty. Like the boastful title of *The Greatest Birth of Time*
it seemed to claim too much for the writer.

However that may be, the autobiographical fragment sup-
plies an illuminating commentary on a letter he wrote about

the same time to his uncle Burghley, the Lord Treasurer, in which, "so far as he could do so without humiliation," he sued for office. "I wax somewhat ancient," he writes; "one-and-thirty years is a great deal of sand in the hourglass." He reminds his uncle that his father had left him unprovided: "The meanness of my estate doth somewhat move me." He tells him, in reference to his philosophical project, that he has "vast contemplative ends." He goes on to explain that he wants to drive out scholastic philosophy and alchemy, and to bring in instead "industrious observations, grounded conclusions, and profitable inventions and discoveries." Humbly he hopes that his motive in all this may be understood to be *philanthropia*, love of mankind. He urges, which is the practical point of the letter, that if he could be given some post "of reasonable countenance" it would bring with it "commandment of more wits than of my own, which is the thing I greatly affect." Bacon is carrying out the conclusion to which he had come in the autobiographical fragment. He is going to try to combine a political career with research into nature. This, with frequent misgivings, remained his aim throughout life.

Before we leave these two documents we may draw attention to a difference of emphasis between the two, which reveals one of the difficulties in which Bacon felt himself involved. His uncle Burghley placed great hopes in alchemy. The devoted Lord Treasurer neglected nothing that might assist the resources of the kingdom. A few years after the battle of the Armada, which is the time with which we are now concerned, a distinguished English alchemist, Dr. John Dee, reported to Burghley that a colleague, Sir Edward Kelly, then practising the art in Prague, had succeeded in transmuting base metal into gold. There was imminent danger of a second attempt at invasion from Spain. With desperate urgency, Burghley wrote pleading that Kelly should not keep the knowledge of this providential discovery from his native land, but that he should "send to her Majesty in some secret box such portion of the powder as might be to her a sum sufficient to defray her charges for this summer for her navy which is now preparing for sea." It was to a man beset with such pressing needs, and a prey to such fond illusions, that his nephew wrote to say, that, given the chance, he hoped to bring in "industrious observations, grounded conclusions, and profitable inventions and discoveries."

To his uncle, then, he stressed the practical advantages that might be promptly expected. But in his private thoughts he entertained much grander hopes. He imagined a more distant but enthralling future for mankind. I quote again from the autobiographical fragment a passage I have reserved till now.

"If a man could succeed not simply in striking out some particular invention, however useful, but in kindling a light in nature—a light which should in its very rising touch and illuminate all the border-regions that confine upon the circle of our present knowledge, and so spreading further and further should presently disclose and bring into view all that is most hidden and secret in the world—that man, I thought, would be the benefactor of the human race, the propagator of man's empire over the universe, the champion of liberty, the conqueror and subduer of necessities."

It was prudent of Bacon, when asking for a job, to suppress these more extravagant hopes. But the two aspects of his vision always remained in his mind, and constituted, as it were, two stages in his plan. Individual inventions and discoveries, he thought, might be quickly come by; but the true goal was to kindle that light in nature that would give man the key to her secret processes and enable him to bring down not one blessing, but a shower of blessings on mankind. Sometimes Bacon seems to think that he had been divinely chosen to be the channel through which God would shower his blessings on the earth.

It must not be thought, however, that these more remote visions, which remind us of the magic of Prospero in the *Tempest*, interfered with his down-to-earth practical activities. Here, for example, are a few of a much longer list of inquiries addressed by Bacon to a distinguished chemist. It is not possible to date the list precisely, but its authenticity is guaranteed by no less a person than Dr. Tenison, Archbishop of Canterbury. An enthusiast for the philosophy of Bacon, he, in 1679, fifty-three years after Bacon's death, published an important volume, *Baconiana or Certain Genuine Remains of Lord Bacon.* The words "This is the clean copy" were found written in Bacon's own hand on the back of the manuscript from which he printed the list. Among the experiments Bacon wanted Dr. Meverel, the chemist, to carry out were these: (1) The compounding of iron with flint for the making of better utensils for the kitchen and for war; (2) compounding iron with brass to produce cheaper utensils than those made of brass alone; (3) increasing the proportion of tin in compounds with brass or copper for the manufacture of instruments "of magnificence and delicacy," like bells and trumpets; (4) varying the ingredients in the manufacture of glass to make it more crystalline, less breakable, and of a greater range and beauty of colors.

We have seen already that Bacon's interest in science had been stimulated by certain modern inventions—the compass, the printing press, and gunpowder. But there was also, apart from these anonymous inventions, a new kind of literature coming into existence that showed that the age was becoming ripe for the Baconian philosophy. As well as translations of the Bible into modern tongues, quite a new kind of literature, the literature of technology, had begun to busy the printers. This did not rest, like the philosophy taught in the universities, on ancient Greek and Latin texts. It depended directly on experience. It was written by men who were actually engaged in the exercise of certain crafts and who had also received sufficient literary education to enable them to record their findings in books.

This was something really new. The only crafts of which descriptions were written down in Greco-Roman antiquity were medicine and architecture. Miners, metallurgists, and potters did not write books. But this is what had now begun to happen. The originality of Bacon is shown by the interest he took in these works, by his appreciation of their novelty, and by his conviction that this was only the beginning of a new development of immense importance for mankind. He had the imagination to grasp the new possibilities. He had also the conscience to insist that it would be a crime to neglect them.

By the year 1540, thirty thousand books had issued from the printing presses. But one book published in that year was the first of its kind. This was *Pirotechnia*, a treatise on metallurgy, by Biringuccio, an Italian. Biringuccio was well aware of his originality. His boast was to have written a book not based on other books but on direct experience of nature. His book was soon well known in England. Richard Eden's *The Decades of the New World* (1555) translated the first three chapters of *Pirotechnia*. Peter Whitehorn's *Certain Waies for the ordering of Souldiers in battleray* (1560) borrows from the same source all that the age knew on mines, bombs, saltpeter, and gunpowder.

Biringuccio's book was promptly followed by a comprehensive treatise on mining and metallurgy, the *De Re Metallica* (1556), by the German Georgius Agricola. He borrowed his account of metallurgy from Biringuccio, added to it an elaborate description of the processes of mining, and illustrated the whole by hundreds of figures of the tools and machines employed. This exact and comprehensive treatise, based on the experience of the German miners in the Tyrol, guided the operations of the Spanish in their exploitation of the mineral wealth of South America, and was found equally useful in England where tin, iron, and coal were being mined in increasing quantities. In England it was read either in the Latin original or in a translation into Italian made by an Italian Protestant refugee who dedicated it to Queen Elizabeth.

The book was much admired by Bacon, whose name is often mentioned in conection with the development of mining in England—a fact which need not surprise us at all, if we remember that no less a man than Sir Walter Raleigh was Warden of the Stannaries (i.e., tin mines) in Cornwall. It would have been important to Bacon not only for its practical usefulness but for its social philosophy. Agricola was a pioneer in preaching the value for civilization of techniques. "If metals were removed from the service of man," he writes, "gone would be all the means of protecting and maintaining health and supporting a civilized mode of life. Without metals men would live a brutish and wretched life on the level of wild beasts. Back they would go to their acorns and berries in the woods." With this we may compare Bacon's own words: "The difference between civilized men and savages is almost that between gods and men. And this difference comes not from soil, not from climate, not from race, but from the arts."

One last example of the pioneers of technology who influenced Bacon remains to be mentioned. When Bacon was at Paris there was in the service of the French king,—as landscape gardener, hydraulic engineer, and general clerk of works—a most remarkable man named Bernard Palissy. He had begun life as a craftsman engaged in the manufacture of colored glass, but early in his career he became possessed with the ambition to discover the jealousy guarded secret of the white enamelled ware manufactured in Italy. The quest occupied him for decades, during which he often worked himself to a standstill and half starved his wife and children. Then, stung by the reproaches of his very active conscience, he would turn himself to some new employment. Here he invariably showed such enterprise and ingenuity that he quickly restored his humble fortunes; but as soon as the home was again furnished and the larder filled, he felt free to return to the old quest.

It must have been hard for his wife to endure. Good money would be spent on new earthenware pots, not for domestic use. Oh, no! He would break them up into small shards, mount on each shard a carefully proportioned mixture of certain chemicals, and ask the hospitality of the potters to bake them in their kilns. Day after day, year in year out, he kept the record of the mixtures employed and the position of each shard in the kiln; until, at long last, one mixture proved right and fused with the earthenware to produce the white enamel he sought. Many manufacturing difficulties still lay ahead, but one day he was master of the full process. Then he became so famous that he soon found himself in the king's household.

But that was not the end. In the course of his various employments, Palissy, with untaught genius, had mastered many secrets in chemistry, geology, botany, and allied subjects. To illustrate his discoveries, he had prepared a museum of natural objects; and one of the wonders of the Court was to attend the lectures he gave to distinguished audiences on the significance of the objects in the museum. We know what the lectures were all about, for Palissy himself has put them on record in one of the most remarkable masterpieces of sixteenth-century scientific literature, the *Discours Admirables* (*Lectures on the Wonders of Nature*) published in 1580. That was the year after Bacon returned again to England. Bacon was therefore at the French Court at the very time when Palissy, his lectures, and his museum, were the fashion of the day.

In the record of Palissy's lectures, we read these memorable words: "I can assure you, dear reader, that in a few hours, in the very first day, you will learn more natural philosophy from the objects displayed in this museum than you could in fifty years devoted to the study of the theories of the ancient philosophers." Here, in simple words, is expressed one of the fundamental principles of the Baconian philosophy. This is what Bacon called "the commerce of the mind with things."

Bacon had gone to France from his studies at Cambridge disgusted with the traditional philosophy because it was "barren of the production of works for the benefit of the life of man." Now here, under his nose, was the example of a man who by direct study of nature had made a whole host of valuable discoveries by which the king himself did not disdain to profit. Bacon does not directly refer to Palissy. It would not have helped his cause to have done so. But those who in recent years have studied the matter closely have no doubt that Bacon had heard at least some of the lectures, and had been in the museum.

Palissy should certainly be included among the pioneers of the new kind of science—the science productive of works—who helped Bacon to formulate his own views. Nor have I any doubt that Bacon, without naming him, does pay homage to the great French craftsman, who had paid such a heavy price for the knowledge he had won. This is the passage I have in mind: "The true and lawful goal of the sciences is simply this, that human life be enriched by new discoveries and powers. The great majority have no feeling for this. Their thoughts never rise above money-making and the routine of their calling. But every now and then it does happen that an exceptionally intelligent and ambitious craftsman applies himself to a new invention, and as a rule, ruins himself in the process." (*Novum Organum* 81) I think Bacon is here using his recollections of Palissy to provide the image of a new type of man emerging in society—a type of man that, as we shall see, he valued very highly.

7

Bacon and Essex

Lord Burghley failed to secure for Francis Bacon the sort of position he sought. But there is no reason to believe, as some say, that he did not press his nephew's claims because he was intent on the advancement of his own son, Robert Cecil. Burghley claimed to have done all he could, and no coolness developed between uncle and nephew. The decision rested with the Queen. It seems certain that she still resented his outspoken opposition in Parliament to her request for a subsidy.

But it is also likely that Bacon's political advancement was retarded precisely by what we now regard as his greatest title to fame. Nobody doubted that he was able and devoted. Nobody doubted that he had studied the business of government and shown aptitude for it. But everybody knew, and Bacon made no secret of the fact, that he wanted office, partly at least, in order to promote his own pet plan of a kingdom enriched and regenerated by his new science. Very few shared this vision, and the few did not include the holders of power. No further explanation is needed of his being passed over for safer and more ordinary men. Only gradually did Bacon himself come to understand the isolation in which his advocacy of his project placed him.

However, he had some followers, and among them was the young, handsome, intelligent, noble-minded, and, as it proved, unstable Earl of Essex. Bacon and Essex had met at the end of 1591 or beginning of 1592, and it was soon apparent that Bacon had found a friend who wholeheartedly believed in him both as statesman and philosopher; and, as Essesx was the Queen's favorite, there was ground for fresh hope that the Queen might also be won around. No other hypothesis will explain the facts. It will be remembered that it was in 1592 and in 1594 that Essex presented before the Queen the "devices" at Gray's Inn in which Bacon had the opportunity to display the attractive outlines of the new philosophy to her Royal Highness. Simultaneously, Essex in private is known to have urged upon the Queen Bacon's claims, first to the office of Attorney General and then to that of Solicitor General.

The Queen refused to listen, but Essex persisted until she was out of patience and he was left with a sense of grievance and humiliation. He even had the feeling that it was his fault that Bacon had been rejected, and he insisted on compensating Bacon for the disappointment by presenting him with a small estate worth about £2,000. It was a generous but not, in fact, very magnificent gift—for Bacon and his brother Anthony had rendered important services to Essex—Francis by his advice on domestic policy, and Anthony, who travelled much on the Continent, by information on foreign affairs. It could have been accepted without humiliation, especially if we bear in mind that, apart from any fees for the offices he held, Essex had in all from the Queen not less than £300,000 for his personal use.

Nevertheless, Bacon resisted the offer, until, as he put it later, Essex pressed it upon him "with so kind and noble circumstance as the manner was more than the matter." But the reason for his reluctance is plain. One so quick in apprehension could not fail to perceive that, however unwillingly, he was becoming involved in a quarrel between Essex and the Queen. He feared a divided loyalty. Accordingly, in a playful phrase which conveyed a serious hint, he accepted the gift with the express caution that, in feudal homage, no obligation to an immediate lord could override the ultimate loyalty to the Throne.

Bacon's fears were well-founded. The rift between the Queen and her chief favorite had begun to open, though nobody could yet foresee that it would end five years later with the execution of Essex for high treason. That terrible conclusion might have been avoided if Essex had been capable of following Bacon's advice; but before we blame him, it would be well to understand how difficult and dangerous was the situation in which he found himself.

Robert Devereux, second Earl of Essex, was born in 1567, being thus six years younger than Bacon. He graduated at Cambridge when he was thirteen, distinguished himself (at the age of eighteen) at the battle of Zutphen, was appointed Master of the Horse two years later, and General of the Horse and a Knight of the Garter at the age of twenty-one. He now faced a danger much greater than the battle of Zutphen. Leicester, the Queen's favorite, under whom Essex had served at Zutphen, died, and the roving fancy of the Queen fastened on Essex. It did not matter to this extraordinary woman that

she was thirty-four years his senior; but how much simpler
for Essex to have been killed at the head of his cavalry! He
was afraid to tell her when he got married two years later,
and when she found out her rage was unbounded. What sort
of creature was she? Francis Bacon can help us understand.

With the rest of his fellow-countrymen he shared a passionate loyalty to the Queen, on whose splended qualities their
country's greatness, even its survival, seemed to depend. As
a tribute to her he composed a Latin writing, *In Felicem
Memoriam Elizabethae*, with instructions for its publication
after his death. The adjective *felix* which he applied to her,
which means lucky or blessed, had a special significance for
him. It meant more than great, for greatness seems to inhere
in the person of the possessor, but luck or blessedness implied
the watchful care of superhuman power. Or possibly, thought
Bacon—and this is perhaps to say the same thing in different
words—good luck is really the consequence of rare qualities
of mind and spirit in the lucky one which escape the understanding of ordinary men. Such persons are, in a sense, beyond
praise, for "praise is the tribute of men, felicity the gift of
God." However he reasoned it out, he left no doubt that, in
his mind, there was a quality in Elizabeth bordering on the
divine.

But he did not on that account suspend his critical faculties.
He never did. Bacon's eulogy left room for frankness, and
nowhere is he more frank than in venturing to raise the question of the Queen's relations with her favorites. It must be
remembered, too, that he was in a degree of nearness to the
Court which allowed him to be well informed. This, then,
is his account: "The Queen permitted herself to be wooed and
courted. Nay, she invited these attentions; she liked the report
of them to be bruited abroad; and she continued to indulge

these amorous attachments when they had long ceased to be becoming to her years. It was a thing much frowned upon by the censorious. Yet, regard them how you will, there is still something in them to stir our wonder. Take the lenient view and you will allow them a fairy-tale quality. They seem to concern some queen in the Islands of the Blest, where the regulation of the court permitted amorous devotion but forbade the gratification of desire. If, on the other hand, you prefer the less kindly view, you will have all the more reason to marvel that these indiscretions neither blackened her good name, nor diminished her queenliness, nor slackened her grasp on the reins of government, nor in any discernible degree retarded her despatch in the conduct of affairs of state."

There were, then, two ways of regarding the Queen's gallantries. You could take her as the symbol of courtly love, as the poet Spenser does. In his *Faery Queen* she is Gloriana, the model of all perfection, the inspirer of knightly deeds. No doubt for a while Essex hoped to be cast in the role of a Spenserian knight. But things did not proceed on this idealistic level, and there was also the more realistic way of regarding her conduct, plainly indicated by Bacon and undoubtedly held by him. It is of more relevance for the understanding of the career of poor Essex.

For, while Essex must have enjoyed the unique position of power and popularity he held at Court, his personal relation with the Queen was irksome to him and he sought opportunities to escape. In 1589, without the consent of the Queen, he joined an expedition against Portugal under Drake, only to be ordered to return immediately. In 1591, he managed to get himself appointed to the command of an auxiliary force to help the French king against the Spaniards. In 1596, he was allowed to share with Lord Howard the command of an expedition against Spain, when they captured and pillaged Cadiz. But every absence weakened his position at home, and Bacon consistently warned him against the risk of allowing himself to be sent to take command of the difficult war against the Irish in Ulster under Hugh O'Neill.

There was a notorious incident in the preliminary discussion of the Irish war. The Queen in council spoke slightingly to Essex. He responded with the unparalleled insult of turning his back on her with a gesture of contempt, and she so far abandoned control of herself as to slap his face. Essex left the council chamber protesting that he would not have brooked such an insult even from Henry VIII.

Already the breach had gone beyond repair. Bacon warned Essex against the risk to his position at home of a long absence in Ireland; but his counsel was no longer heeded. Essex did go to Ireland, where he bungled the war, disobeyed instructions, gave offence by his presumption in creating a great number of knights, and finally came home without leave. His course of conduct rapidly assumed a more and more treasonable air. His secretary, Sir Thomas Smith (who incidentally was one of Bacon's friends), now found it necessary to keep himself aloof from his intrigues. Egerton, the Lord Keeper, a tried friend of both Bacon and Essex, had sent two sons to serve under Essex, in Ireland. He, too, warned him privately of the ill favor with which his conduct in Ireland was regarded at court, and might have hoped to retain some influence over him. But as Essex was progressively deprived by the Queen of the revenues he owed to her bounty and of his privileges, he seems to have come to regard his personal predicament as a national crisis. He hatched some absurd plot to seize the Queen's person, force her to change her advisers, and so return to power. When Egerton was sent to his house to inquire into the truth behind these rumors, Essex locked him in a back room. He then sallied out into the streets with a small company of armed men, in the expectation of raising a large following in the city for an attack on the palace. He was arrested, tried, and condemned. The old Queen, whose hesitations it would take a Shakespeare to imagine, at last gave a reluctant assent to his execution. Her handsome favorite was thirty-three.

Essex's friends, and particularly Francis Bacon, have been reproached for their part in his death. Sir Thomas Smith played the minor role of summoning him before the Privy Council. Egerton, by virtue of his position, had no option but to play a prominent role at the trial. Bacon held a watching brief for the Queen, one of whose law advisers he was. He made two interventions, cutting through a tangle of irrelevant circumstances to bring the court back to the essentially treasonable element in the actions of his friend. It must have been one of the heaviest days in his life, but there was no question for him of divided loyalties. He stood where he had always stood. He has himself stated the principle on which he acted. It should be repeated here as his sufficient explanation of his part in the affair. "My defence," he wrote, in reply to those who impugned his action, "needeth to be but simple and brief: namely, that whatever I did concerning that action and proceeding was done in my duty and service to the Queen and State; in which I would not show myself false-hearted nor faint-hearted for any man's sake living. For every honest man that hath his heart well planted will forsake his King rather than forsake God, and forsake his friend rather than forsake his King; and yet will forsake any earthly commodity, yea and his own life in some cases, rather than forsake his friend."

8

"Some Sorry Book-Maker"

The execution of Essex took place in 1601, but any hope that Essex could help Bacon to a government post had faded long before, and, as his political hopes declined, Bacon began to turn his thoughts to writing. The first we hear of this is in the letter of 1591 in which he asks his uncle Burghley to do what he can for him. Toward the end of that letter he remarks that, if no place can be found for him, he will sell his property, take steps to turn the proceeds into a small fixed income, "and so give over all care of service [i.e., work in the service of the Queen] and become some sorry book-maker." Such were the contemptuous terms in which he then referred to the career of an author. But this was only a temporary bitterness. Two years later in a letter to his cousin, Robert Cecil, Lord Burghley's son, he announces the same decision, but this time with a becoming pride in the new career he has chosen: "My ambition now I shall put only upon my pen, whereby I shall be able to maintain memory and merit of the times succeeding."

Of his ability to write he had already given abundant proof, and he was justified in anticipating future fame. But the proof had been given in semiprivate papers directed to the formulation of public policy on the great questions of the day. In what way they were circulated and how widely they were known is not easy to decide. One such paper, written about 1589, is called *An Advertisement touching the Controversies of the Church.*

The subject is religious toleration. It had become important by reason both of the breach with Rome and also of the rise of many dissenting sects. Bacon's own position was that of the Anglican Church. He wanted the King and not the Pope to be head. He preferred government by bishops to government by elders (as in the Presbyterian Church in Scotland and elsewhere). He looked to the Scriptures as the sole source of revelation and to the practice of the first four or five centuries of Christianity as the pattern of church discipline. He saw the advantages of uniformity of belief and practice, and hoped for the establishment of a fully national church. He was suspicious of the systems of doctrine and church government recently hatched out in continental centers in Germany and Switzerland. But his own mother was a Calvinist, and he understood the strength of Puritan feeling. He could admire the passionate loyalty of the Jesuits to the older form of the faith, while counting on the zeal of the Puritan preachers to support the principles of the Reformation. He feared that, if the Puritans were handled without sympathy, they would go on to overthrow the Church of England as they had overthrown the Church of Rome.

The fears were well grounded. The discords were not

overcome. Under James I and Charles I, the established Church came to be identified with the party supporting government by the prerogative of the King, while the dissenters, the Puritans, became the party of national liberty. This breach in the religious life of the nation, which still persists today, was just beginning to open when Bacon wrote, and the tone of the controversialists was becoming violent and scurrilous in the extreme.

A few sentences will suffice to make clear the wise and tolerant temper in which Bacon sought to heal the wounds and save the national unity. "The controversies themselves I will not enter into as judging that the disease requireth rest rather than any other cure. . . . If we would but remember that the ancient and true bonds of unity are one faith, one baptism, and not one ceremony, one policy . . . if we did but know the virtue of silence and slowness to speak, commended by St James; our controversies of themselves would close up and grow together . . . God grant that we may contend with other churches, as the vine with the olive, which of us beareth the best fruit, and not as the brier with the thistle, which of us is most unprofitable."

"And first of all," he goes on, "it is more than time that there were an end and surseance made of this immodest and deformed manner of writing lately entertained, whereby matters of religion are handled in the style of the stage. Indeed, bitter and earnest writing may not be hastily condemned, for men cannot contend coldly and without affection about things which they hold dear and precious. A politic man may write from his brain without touch and sense of his heart, as in a speculation that pertaineth not unto him; but a feeling Christian will express in his words a character either of zeal or love. The latter of which as I could wish rather

Sir Nicholas Bacon as Lord Keeper. This portrait was painted in 1579, the year of his death.

(*Above*) Sir Nicholas's house at Gorhambury which, in 1579, Francis
dreamed was plastered over with black plaster. (*Below*) *The Great
Harry*, an Elizabethan Man-of-War, at about the time of the Armada

embraced, being more fit for these times, yet is the former also warranted by great examples. But to leave all reverent and religious compassion towards evils, or indignation towards faults, and to turn religion into a comedy or a satire; to search and rip up wounds with a laughing countenance; to intermix Scripture and scurrility sometimes in one sentence; is a thing far from the devout reverence of a Christian, and scant becoming the honest regard of a sober man."

The perfection of tone and temper in this piece of writing, its eloquence and force, its breadth of learning and its relevance to the immediate issue, were too remarkable to be ignored, and, though he was not given a place, the service of his pen was often called upon. Thus when some disaffected person, probably the Jesuit Parsons, wrote an attack on Burghley's administration, alleging that England had fallen into poverty and disorder since the quarrel with the Pope, it was Bacon again who was called upon to draft a reply. This *Observations on a Libel,* as it is called, is quite a sizeable document, about twenty-five thousand words, covering religion, law, administration of justice, and many other things.

One passage is worth quoting here, it gives such a charming sketch of the growing wealth of the country at this period of rapid change. "There was never the like number of fair and stately houses as have been built and set up from the ground since her Majesty's reign. . . . There were never the like pleasures of goodly gardens and orchards, walks, pools, and parks, as do adorn almost every mansion house. . . . There was never the like quantity of waste and unprofitable ground inned, reclaimed, and improved. . . . The towns were never better built nor peopled; nor the principal fairs and markets never bettered customed nor frequented. . . . The commodities and eases of rivers cut by the hand and brought into

a new channel, of piers that have been built, of waters that
have been forced and brought against the ground, were never
so many. There were never so many new handicrafts used
and exercised, nor new commodities made within the realm:
as sugar, paper, glass, copper, divers silks, and the like." We
can see that Bacon had studied hard to grasp all the rich
detail of every aspect of the life of the country he had hoped
to be able to play a part in governing.

But now these hopes were dead. There remained, however,
the career of an inventor or discoverer of new arts, which he
had already declared to be nobler than that of a statesman
because its benefits extended to all mankind. To this he would
devote himself, and the path to it seemed to lie through
writing. He needed authority and influence. If he could not
acquire it by virtue of some high office, he might earn it by
his pen. To this, therefore, he applied himself. He had by
him a small collection of *Essays* in English and of *Sacred
Meditations* in Latin, which had circulated in manuscript,
been much admired, and were about to be pirated. These he
gathered into a little volume and had it printed himself, with
a dedication to Anthony. "Loving and beloved brother, I
do now like some that have an orchard ill-neighboured, that
gather their fruit before it is ripe, to prevent stealing." The
date was 1597. Francis Bacon was thirty-six years old. It was
his first book.

First a word about the *Sacred Meditations*. Characteristically they concern themselves more with practical morality
than with private devotion. In one of the most interesting,
Bacon raises the case of a man who does not aspire simply to
a solitary goodness, but aims at what he calls "a fructifying
and begetting good" which affects also the lives of others.
This is plainly only another way of referring to his project

for a new kind of philosophy that would bring about "the relief of man's estate." For a man with such an ambition it will not be enough, says Bacon, that his intentions should be good. As well as the innocence of the dove he will need the wisdom of the serpent; for the world in which he will have to work is a wicked world, and if he is to get anywhere, a reformer will need to know his way about in the midst of the cynicism and villainy which everywhere abound.

In another, Bacon takes as his model the Jesus of the Gospels, who "restored motion to the lame, light to the blind, speech to the dumb, health to the sick, cleanness to the lepers, sound mind to them that were possessed with devils, life to the dead." Bacon also shows how to expose hypocrites. Their habit is to make a great display of devotion in public, which costs them nothing. In order to expose them, they should be directed toward works of mercy and reminded that "pure religion and undefiled is this, to visit the widows and orphans in their affliction and keep oneself unspotted by the world." Such is the chief message of the *Meditations.* They reveal Bacon as a zealous but realistic philanthropist.

The *Essays*, in the 1597 edition, numbered only ten. But they had a great success, which pleased their author, and he continued to build on them throughout his life. In a new edition in 1612, their number had gone up to thirty-eight. In the third and last edition published by the author (it came out in 1625, the year before his death), the total had risen to fifty-eight. Thus they occupied Bacon's attention for some thirty years, and they constitute, perhaps, his best claim to be a philosopher in the popular sense of the term, that is, a man who can think more wisely than his fellows on all the various contingencies of life.

9

The Essays

Of his *Essays* Bacon says in one of several dedications: "My hope is, that they may be as grains of salt that will rather give you an appetite than offend you with satiety. And although they handle those things wherein both men's lives and their pens are most conversant, yet (what I have attained I know not) but I have endeavoured to make them not vulgar, but of a nature whereof a man shall find much in experience little in books; so as they are neither repetitions nor fancies." They sprang out of his own experience, and his hope was, to use another of his expressions, that they would "come home to men's business and bosoms." I propose to devote this chapter to some quotations from the *Essays* in which he speaks his mind on morality, religion, politics, law, and culture. There is a story that when the miniaturist Hilliard had made his portrait of Francis Bacon, he wrote below it in Latin, "If only I could paint his mind." In this brief anthology of quotations Bacon will paint his own mental image for us.

Of Goodness and Goodness of Nature

I take goodness in this sense, the affecting of the weal of men, which is what the Grecians called *philanthropia;* and the word humanity, as it is used, is a little too light to express it. Goodness I call the habit, and goodness of nature the inclination. This of all virtues and dignities of the mind is the greatest, being the character of the Deity; and without it man is a busy, mischievous, wretched thing, no better than a kind of vermin. Goodness answers to the theological virtue charity, and admits no excess but error. The desire of power in excess caused the angels to fall; the desire of knowledge in excess caused man to fall; but in charity there is no excess, neither can angel or man come in danger by it.

Of Wisdom for a Man's Self

Wisdom for a man's self is in many branches thereof a depraved thing. It is the wisdom of rats, that will be sure to leave a house somewhat before it falls. It is the wisdom of the fox, that thrusts out the badger who digged and made room for him. It is the wisdom of crocodiles, that shed tears when they would devour.

Of Atheism

I had rather believe all the fables in the Legend, and the Talmud, and the Alcoran, than that this universal frame is without a mind. And therefore God never wrought miracle to convince atheism, because his ordinary works convince it. It is true that a little philosophy inclineth men's minds to atheism, but depth in philosophy bringeth men's minds about to religion. For while the mind of man looketh on second causes scattered, it may sometimes rest in them and go no further; but when it beholdeth the chain of them confederate and linked together, it must needs fly to providence and deity.

Of the True Greatness of Kingdoms

Let states that aim at greatness take heed how their nobility and gentlemen do multiply too fast. For that maketh the common subject grow to be a peasant and base swain, driven out of heart, and in effect but the gentleman's labourer. Even as you may see in coppice woods, if you leave your staddles too thick, you shall never have clean underwood, but shrubs and bushes. So in countries, if the gentlemen be too many, the commons will be base; and you will bring it to that, that not the hundredth poll will be fit for an helmet.

Of Riches

Of great riches there is no real use except it be in the distribution. The rest is but conceit. . . . Seek not proud riches, but such as thou mayest get justly, use soberly, distribute cheerfully, leave contentedly. Yet have no abstract nor friarly contempt of them. . . . The ways to enrich are many and most of them foul. Parsimony is one of the best, and yet it is not innocent, for it withholdeth men from works of liberality and charity. The improvement of the ground is the most natural obtaining of riches. For it is our Great Mother's blessing, the Earth's. But it is slow. And yet, where men of great wealth do stoop to husbandry, it multiplieth riches exceedingly. I knew a nobleman in England that had the greatest audits of any man in my time—a great grazier, a great sheep-master, a great timber-man, a great collier, a great corn-master, a great lead-man, and so of iron, and a number of the like points of husbandry. So as the earth seemed a sea to him in respect of the perpetual importation. . . . Usury is the certaintest means of gain, though one of the worst, as that whereby a man doth eat his bread *in sudore vultus alieni* (in the sweat of another's brow), and besides doth plough upon sundays.

Of Revenge

Revenge is a kind of wild justice, which the more man's nature runs to the more ought law to weed it out. For as for the first wrong, it doth but offend the law; but the revenge of that wrong putteth the law out of office.

Of Plantations (i.e., Colonies)

I like plantation in a pure soil, that is, where people are not displanted to the end to plant in others. For else it is rather an extirpation than a plantation. . . . The people wherewith you plant ought to be gardeners, ploughmen, labourers, smiths, carpenters, joiners, fishermen, fowlers, with some few apothecaries, surgeons, cooks, and bakers. . . . When the plantation grows to strength, then is the time to plant with women as well as with men, that the plantation may spread into generations and not be ever pieced from without. It is the sinfullest thing in the world to forsake or destitute a plantation once in forwardness. For besides the dishonour it is the guiltiness of blood of many commiserable persons.

Of Gardens

God Almighty first planted a garden. And indeed it is the purest of human pleasures. It is the greatest refreshment to the spirits of man, without which buildings and palaces are but gross handiworks. And a man shall ever see that when ages grow to civility and elegance, men come to build stately sooner than to garden finely; as if gardening were the greater perfection.

Of Studies

Studies serve for delight, for ornament, and for ability. Their chief use for delight is in privateness and retiring, for ornament is in discourse, and for ability is in the judgment and disposition of business. . . . Crafty men condemn studies, simple men admire them, and wise men use them. For they teach not their own use, but that is a wisdom without them and above them, won by observation.

Of Unity in Religion

Concerning the means of procuring unity, men must beware that in the procuring of religious unity they do not dissolve and deface the laws of charity and of humane society . . . and that they do not so consider men as Christians as to forget that they are men. Lucretius the poet, when he beheld the act of Agamemnon, that could endure the sacrificing of his own daughter, exclaimed *Tantum religio potuit suadere malorum* (such wickedness could religion drive men to). What would he have said if he had known of the massacre in France or the powder treason of England? He would have been seven times more Epicure and atheist than he was.

Of Death

It is as natural to die as to be born; and to a little infant, perhaps, the one is as painful as the other. He that dies in an earnest pursuit is like one that is wounded in hot blood, who, for the time, scarce feels the hurt. And therefore a mind fixed and bent upon somewhat that is good doth avert the dolours of death. But above all, believe it, the sweetest canticle is *Nunc dimittis* (Lord, now lettest thou thy servant depart in peace), when a man hath obtained worthy ends and expectations. Death hath this also, that it openeth the gate to good fame and extinguisheth envy. *Extinctus amabitur idem* (Love will follow him beyond the grave).

IO

Working in Isolation

The *Essays* were an immediate success. It was plain that if Bacon confined himself to discussing religion, politics, and culture, he could easily win popularity and esteem. But it was equally plain that his philosophy of works, which was his chief concern, was not appreciated and aroused little interest. It was more than probable, indeed, that it had been the chief obstacle to his advancement. New ideas are not usually welcomed. All sorts of objections to it were raised. Some said it was impossible, otherwise it would have been done before. Others thought it a threat to religion. If God wanted man to know the secrets of nature, why had He taken such pains to hide them? Yet others thought it illiberal: it involved endless tiresome occupation with the details of humble arts and crafts, grubbing after sordid details, instead of letting the speculative reason have free play as philosophers had been accustomed to do.

Bacon felt himself completely isolated. He was driven in upon himself. He felt the need both to state his case more convincingly, and also to understand why men had such difficulty in accepting what seemed to him so obviously true and desirable. Accordingly, the next ten or twelve years of his life were spent in wrestling with these problems.

As soon as he saw light in any direction he began to write, sometimes in English but mostly in Latin. Many of these writings were left unfinished. Others were finished but left unpublished. And the two which he did publish, *The Advancement of Learning* (1605) and the *De Sapientia Veterum* (*On the Wisdom of the Ancients*) (1609), speak guardedly about the scientific revolution which was nearest to his heart —so conscious had he become of the hostility or indifference with which his project was received. In fact it was not until his political fortunes had culminated under James I and he had been made Lord Chancellor that he felt in a strong enough position to throw down his ringing challenge to the world. Only then did he present his argument and his plea in the most direct and forceful language he could command; only then did he venture to publish his masterpiece, *The Great Instauration.*

That was in 1620, but he had thought of the title twenty years before, and it is important to understand all he meant by it. In ancient Rome, when some great enterprise began to go amiss owing to neglect of some divine injunction, the practice was to abandon it completely, take the auspices again (that is, consult again the will of the gods), and then make a completely new start in conformity with the divine will. This was called an *instauratio,* and this is Bacon's meaning of the term. He pointed out that God had promised man dominion over the creation. Why, then, does man not enjoy this dominion? It is, said Bacon, because of the sin of pride. The philosophers have presumed to suppose that they could learn the secrets of nature without taking the trouble to study the book of nature. They have proudly spun theories out of their own heads instead of humbly acquainting themselves with the facts.

We must, then, said Bacon, make a fresh beginning in accordance with the divine will. God is the author of two books—the Bible, and Nature. The Bible reveals to man the will of God, which is that we should walk humbly before Him and love our neighbors as ourselves. Nature, God's other book, reveals His power. But this we can read aright only if we become as little children, abandon our presumptuous dream of conjuring up a picture of the universe out of our own minds, and humbly devote ourselves to the study of the book of nature. If we do this, we may trust that we shall enjoy the blessing that was taken from Adam after the Fall.

The Baconian philosophy, the philosophy of works, is thus in a double sense a religious obligation. To study the book of nature is to come to know the power of God. To apply the knowledge so gained to the relief of man's estate is to carry out God's will. Science and service of mankind were thus inseparably linked in Bacon's mind by the very doctrine of the Creation. For ourselves we may add that, whether we find Bacon's religion acceptable or not, all experience of applied science since his day has gone to show that in itself it is neither good nor bad. Everything depends on the use we make of it. Mechanical power is no substitute for morality.

The religious objections to his project thus swept away, we may consider how Bacon dealt with the problem of scepticism, the readiness of men to call his project impossible, their inability to understand what his proposal was about. To begin with, this made him impatient and even a little contemptuous. He was filled with moral indignation, for instance, when he considered the readiness of doctors to call so many diseases incurable instead of trying to find the cure. This seemed to him to be simply blaming nature when the fault really lay with the art of medicine.

But it was much more maddening to think of the whole long history of philosophy in which men had been willing to argue the rights and wrongs of their speculations about nature without ever asking themselves how to master nature's laws and apply them to the improvement of the conditions of life. This seemed to Bacon to be nothing less than "universal madness," and when he reflected on "the immeasurable helplessness and poverty of the human race," the contrast between the desperateness of the need and the complacency of the philosophers filled him with searing indignation.

The outcome of this was a blistering attack in one of his unfinished writings on many of the great names in the history of thought. It is characteristic that he did not publish it. Having gotten it off his chest, he set it aside and tried to think about the problem in a more helpful way. The result was a brilliant analysis of the difficulties that necessarily beset the human mind in its endeavor to arrive at a true knowledge of nature.

These difficulties arise from several causes. First, there is the very nature of man himself. Man has only a limited equipment of senses and limited powers of thought; inevitably he makes up for himself a picture of the universe which is cut according to the measure of his capacity and is very far indeed from being the whole or the undistorted truth. Then there is the fact that the individual human being is conditioned by his circumstances and his education. A savage and a civilized man, a solitary monk in his cell and a world-voyager, a ploughman and a courtier, will not think the same way.

Then there is the difficulty of language. Language has been fashioned to deal with the ordinary affairs of everyday life, or with traditional ways of looking at things. When we try to build up a quite new kind of knowledge, we are held back by the looseness, vagueness, inaccuracy, and conventional meaning of all the terms in use.

Finally, there is the cultural fact that certain systems of thought, elaborated without reference to the problem of the *control* of nature, have acquired enormous prestige, are accepted as true, and taught in the universities. The hallmark of a liberal education in Bacon's day was one's familiarity with this mode of thought.

From these four sources sprang illusory ideas of the nature of reality. Bacon called them *Idols*, because they were false, and gave them the fanciful names of Idols of the Tribe, Idols of the Cave, Idols of the Market-Place, and Idols of the Theatre.

The doctrine of Idols, which is a psychological analysis of various types of illusory thinking, was then amplified by being combined with a sketch of the history of learning. Bacon no longer attacked individual thinkers, but he tried to define the limitations to which great thinkers at various periods of civilization must necessarily be subject. Thus the Greeks, though they were so brilliant, did not know as much history as the moderns nor had they visited as much of the surface of the globe. Confined to their small city-states, and not over-occupied with administration, they devoted themselves to speculation and argument. The practical side of life they relegated as far as they could to slaves. So far as natural philosophy, therefore, is concerned, their stock of experience was

Frontispiece of *Instauratio
Magna*, Bacon's masterpiece
of 1620

Lord Burghley with his son,
Robert Cecil, Lord Salisbury

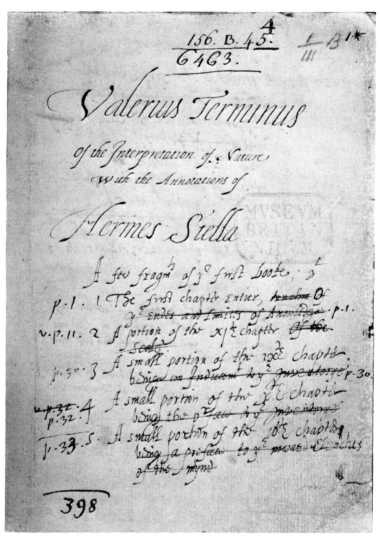

Title page and list of contents of *Valerius Terminus* (1603).
Everything except the title is in Bacon's own hand.

Of the Interpretacion

p. 34 . 6 . A small portion of the iiij^th chapter
~~of the~~ ~~mixed mℓs~~ ~~of Knowledg in generall~~

p. 35 . 7th A small portion of the vth chapter ~~of the~~
~~division of sciences~~

p. 37 . 8 The vij^th chapter Entire

p. 39 . 9 A portion of the viij^th Chapter .

p. 41 . 10 The viiij^th chapter Entire

p. 46 . 11 Another portion of the ix^th chapter p. 46 .

12 The Abridgmt of the 12. 13. 14. 15. 16. 17.
p. 49. &c . 18. 19. 21. 22. 25. 26th chapters
of y^e first booke

13 . The first chapter of ~~the~~ a booke of
the same argumt written in Latine
and destined ~~for~~ to be ~~traditionary~~ separate and
not published .

Some of y^e ffimitations of Stile
are sett down in these fragmenty

Frontispiece of the first *History of the Royal Society*. The President, Lord Brouncker, and Francis Bacon, its chief inspiration, sit on either side of a bust of Charles II, founder and patron of the Society.

limited, their inclination was to pursue new arguments rather than new arts, and their knowledge of material things was confined to their appearances since the manipulation of them was in the hands of slaves or despised craftsmen.

So for other times and places. The Romans first conquered and then administered a vast empire. They can teach us the arts of war and government, but not science. The early Church was too absorbed in the next world to be able to give much thought to this one. We can go to them for theology but not natural philosophy. The men of the Reformation were seeking to correct the abuses of the Church in their own day by reviving the knowledge of the first four Christian centuries. We can look to them for a knowledge of dead languages and of books for "delicate learning," to use Bacon's choice phrase, but not for the robust kind of knowledge sought by the author of *The Greatest Birth of Time*.

In this way Bacon rescued himself from the futility of attacking individual thinkers, and created in place of it a preliminary sketch of that branch of inquiry which is now called the history of ideas, or the sociology of knowledge. And in the light of this historical approach, he eventually managed to make his public understand the essential newness, originality, and purpose of his great reform. Such were the achievements of the lonely isolated years of thought in which he published nothing and made no great figure in the world outside Parliament.

It remains to say a word about the accusation that his philosophy, in contrast with what was taught in the universities, was illiberal in that it involved contact with the detailed practice of the humblest arts and crafts. It will be remembered that the works of the metallurgist Biringuccio, the mining engineer Agricola, and the potter Palissy had profoundly influenced Bacon's thought. In fact, one of the most hopeful and wholesome things in the England of Bacon's day was that contact and cooperation between gentlefolk and technicians was becoming respectable.

At this time lived one Gabriel Harvey, the friend of the poet Spenser and a great admirer of Francis Bacon. He has left us some pertinent reflections on this theme. He, as it happened, was the son of a ropemaker, and finding himself attacked by some literary snobs on this account, he broke out in the following terms (the date was 1593): "He that remembereth Humphrey Cole a mathematical mechanician, Matthew Baker a shipwright, John Shute an architect, Robert Norman a navigator, William Bourne a gunner, John Hester a chymist, or any like cunning and subtle empirique, is a proud man if he contemn expert artisans, or any sensible industrious practitioners, howsoever unlectured in schools or unlettered in books."

Bacon was an enthusiastic supporter of this view. He was calling for a new philosophy and proclaiming at this very date that one of the fundamental elements in it must be "mechanical history or the history of the arts, to which no man has ever applied himself, on which no man has ever expended the unbroken toil which is its due."

II

To Publish or Not to Publish

While Bacon was hammering out the ideas described in the last chapter, the life of the old Queen was drawing to its close. In 1603, she died, "departing this life mildly, like a lamb; easily, like a ripe apple from the tree," to quote the phrase of a diarist of this golden age of English prose. Bacon's loyalty and admiration were unshaken, but he must sometimes have reflected sadly that it was about thirty-five years since she had called him her "young Lord Keeper," and that now at forty-two he was still plain Mr. Bacon. It was gratifying therefore to learn that he was to be included in a group of knights to be created by the new King to grace his coronation. But to be only one of a group—that was a little humiliating. He wrote to his cousin Robert Cecil, a younger and less able man, who was now chief of the Secretaries of State, to ask that, if possible, some special distinction might enhance the occasion. "For my knighthood, I wish the manner might be such as might grace me, since the matter will not; I mean that I might not be gregarious in a troop." But that is just what he was, gregarious in a troop. He was knighted at Whitehall on the 23rd of July, two days before the coronation, along with three hundred others!

It had been a long slow journey to reach the lowest rung of the ladder. Still, his prospects had brightened and the old desire for office again awoke. James had a reputation for learning to rival that of Elizabeth. Was it not possible that his mind might be more open to new ideas? Bacon had lost none of his reforming zeal, so he resolved to try. But he had learned by bitter experience that he could not expect others to share his views. He knew now what Idols blocked men's minds against the light. He remembered how "Mr. Bacon in praise of knowledge" had made no perceptible impression on the mind of Elizabeth. If he was to lay successful siege to the mind of James he needed some more powerful engine. The outcome of these thoughts was the writing of one of his most famous works, *The Advancement of Learning*. It is ironical to reflect that it owed its success to the care Bacon took *not* to express in it the whole of his thought.

The book, which seems to have been quickly written, came out in 1605 with a flattering dedication to the King. Its purpose was, first, to praise the excellency of learning and knowledge; second, to describe the steps taken in the past to advance knowledge; and, third, to point out the insufficiency of these steps and how they might be improved and made more effective.

The first two objects presented no difficulty. The praise of learning and the history of learning were subjects after Bacon's own heart, and what he had to say about them could be expected to interest and delight the King. The trouble came with the third part, the steps that still remained to be taken in order to outstrip the past and raise knowledge to a new level of efficiency. Here Bacon would have to tread lightly. He knew King James to be a learned theologian; he had no reason to suppose he had read Biringuccio, Agricola, or Palissy and shared their enthusiasm for what metallurgy, mining, and other humble trades and arts might contribute to human well-being. Bacon's tactic, therefore, was to drop only a few strong hints on this subject, in the hope that they might fall like seeds on fertile soil.

Thus he early seizes an opportunity to direct the attention of the wise King James to the example of the wise King Solomon, whose interest in science is with Bacon a constant theme. "Nay, the same Solomon the king, although he excelled in the glory of treasure and magnificent buildings, of shipping and navigation, of service and attendance, of fame and renown, and the like, yet he maketh no claim to any of these glories, but only to the glory of the inquisition of truth; for so he saith expressly, *The glory of God is to conceal a thing, but the glory of the king is to find it out;* as if, according to the innocent play of children, the Divine Majesty took delight to hide his works, to the end to have them found out; and as if kings could not obtain a greater honour than to be God's playfellows in that game; considering their great commandment of wits and means, whereby nothing needeth to be hid from them."

When the King had been thus taught the lesson that only kings had adequate resources to go in for science, Bacon then breaks the news that in his, Bacon's, considered opinion the really serious research must be done on the mechanical arts. He complains that in the past men rejected familiar and vulgar experiments, because they felt it to be a kind of dishonor to learning to descend to inquiry or meditation upon mechanical things. "But if my judgment be of any weight, the use of history mechanical [i.e., of research into the subject matter of the mechanical arts] is of all others the most radical and fundamental towards natural philosophy; such natural philosophy as shall not vanish in the fume of subtle, sublime, or delectable speculation, but such as shall be operative to the endownment and benefit of man's life."

This is a clear and uncompromising proclamation of Bacon's position, as far as it goes. But it stands in isolation, it lacks development, its implications are not drawn out. And this is the reason why Bacon later described the *Advancement* as being only "a preparative or key for the opening of the *Instauration*," adding that it was a "mixture of new conceits and old," while the *Instauration* alone contained "the new unmixed." Bacon, then, prudently pulled his punches in the *Advancement*, but that should not make us underestimate the importance of this great book which contains many splendid things. Its main theme is a spirited defence of learning on the ground that learning induces in men a willingness to devote themselves to the public service and the capacity to do so wisely and disinterestedly.

"Only learned men," he writes, "love business as an action according to nature. . . . Of all men they are the most indefatigable, if it be towards any business which can hold or detain their mind." And in a typically Baconian phrase, in which feeling and intellect are present in equal measure, and where the expression is as terse as it is beautiful, he insists that learning "endues the mind with a tender sense and fast obligation of duty." This truth he exemplified in his own life.

In this book also he brilliantly challenged the current notion that an opinion, because it is ancient, must be true. We are accustomed to associate wisdom with antiquity; but if we do that, we should realize that what are called ancient times were really the youth of the world. It is we who deserve, by reason of our accumulated experience, to be credited with the greater wisdom, for as the world grows older it should become wiser. This stimulating thought emancipated the minds of many in his day from the fetters of the past and gave them confidence to believe in the possibility of wholesome change.

Bacon was fully conscious, however, that he had not discharged his conscience by writing the *Advancement*. It was only a preparation for the new philosophy which in a passionate phrase he called "his only earthly wish." Accordingly he set to work at once to expound his message, so far as it had now become clear to him, fully, explicitly, and with all the force at his command. The outcome of this endeavor was two short but very meaty little books in Latin, of which the English titles are *Thoughts and Conclusions* and *Refutation of Philosophies*. These are not fragments like the works discussed in the last chapter, but complete and carefully polished compositions, as good as any he ever wrote. Having written them, however, Bacon, who was now proceeding with extreme caution, decided to submit them to the judgment of his friends before risking publication. He did not want them to fall on barren ground.

Three of these friends are known to us. One was the young Tobie Matthew, who after the death of Anthony, entered more closely than anybody else into Francis's literary plans. Their relation to one another is interesting. Tobie was the son of the Anglican bishop of Durham; and, after helping Francis with his advice during the composition of the *Advancement*, he had gone to spend a couple of years on the

Continent. From there he returned with the news that he
had become a Roman Catholic. This was an embarrassment
to his friends and, so soon after the Gunpowder Plot, to the
authorities. Francis thought that his credulity had been prac-
tised upon, and told him so. But he also told him that his
friendship remained unaltered. This was true. They remained
close friends till Francis died, and the essay on *Friendship*,
which appeared only in the last edition and was written at
the request of Tobie, is a monument to the warmth and sin-
cerity of their relation. The authorities, after an effort to have
Tobie reconverted, put some restraint on his liberty for six
months, and then required him to leave England and live
abroad. However, there seems no doubt that Francis was
able to have his advice about *Thoughts and Conclusions* and
Refutation of Philosophies; that Tobie strongly approved;
and that this was all the encouragement that Francis got.

Another whom he consulted was Lancelot Andrewes, a
man five or six years older than Bacon, and a friend of long
standing. Of all the creators of the Anglican tradition, Bishop
Lancelot Andrewes was the most revered for the saintliness
of his life and the devotional richness of his sermons. A brilliant linguist, he was the leading personality among the trans-
lators who at this time were engaged in preparing the
authorized version of the Bible. He was also, at the request
of King James, employed in the less congenial task of theological controversy with Cardinal Bellarmine. No doubt his
hands were full. Anyway, so far as is known, no word of
encouragement from him reached Francis Bacon. It is very
probable he was not much in sympathy, though Bacon noted
him down in his diary as "a friend to experiments." Indeed,
he may have genuinely felt out of his depth, for he was a man
of the utmost modesty, and his learning, which had been

centered on divinity, would probably have been classed by his friend Francis as "delicate learning." From the letter Francis wrote to him on sending his manuscript, it seems clear that the most he hoped from him was some comment and criticism on the Latin style.

What was decisive for Bacon was the adverse opinion of his third friend, Sir Thomas Bodley, the founder of the great library at Oxford that bears his name. Here was a man of weight, whose opinion might be considered representative of the educated elite of the day. His kindly expressed and carefully considered verdict was that Bacon was wrong and that there was not a responsible academic body in the kingdom that could be found to support his proposals. The most disheartening thing about it was not the condemnation, but the fact that it rested on a complete failure to understand what Bacon was talking about. If Bodley could not understand him, who would? The time was not yet ripe. The two choice writings were set aside to await publication after his death.

But it must not be thought that Bacon was defeated. If public opinion was not yet prepared to accept his plan, then his duty was to prepare it. Accordingly he planned another book which, like the *Advancement,* should be a mixture of old and new. This, stylistically the most brilliant of his Latin writings, bore the unexpected title of *On the Wisdom of the Ancients.* There is something almost laughable about this at first sight, for Bacon's theme-song in his unpublished writings had been just the reverse; in them he had insisted over and over again that science must be sought not in ancient books but in direct contact with nature. What, then, is the explanation of this apparently unaccountable change? It is not difficult to understand.

What people generally meant when they spoke of the

ancients was the philosophy of Plato and Aristotle. This philosophy had been and continued to be the object of his attack. But Bacon had meanwhile been reading widely and deeply, and had come to understand that in the period of Greek philosophy that preceded Plato and Aristotle there were many great thinkers who held opinions much nearer to his own. The most important of these was the atomic philosopher Democritus. Bacon thought that this philosophy provided a much more hopeful foundation for natural science than that of Plato and Aristotle; in his opinion, Plato had made a mistake in mingling theology with natural philosophy, and Aristotle had made an even worse mistake in relying on logic to the neglect of experience. In his *Wisdom of the Ancients,* Bacon cuts the ground from under the feet of Plato and Aristotle by going back to something still more ancient than they, namely, the atomic system. This, of course, as everybody knows, did prove in course of time the best foundation for modern chemistry and physics.

But atomism is neither the main topic nor the most ancient one with which Bacon was concerned in this book. Behind the oldest Greek writings there lies something much older still, a copious mythology on which the earliest poets draw. For some time, Italian scholars had been exercising their wits in studying this mythology and seeking to understand what authority should be allowed it. For undoubtedly it often seems to suggest a sort of wisdom to which we have lost the key. Bacon also was intensely interested in this problem. He was much too honest to pretend to have solved it, but it struck him forcibly that many of the oldest myths could be interpreted in such a way as to lend to his own novel views the support of the most remote antiquity.

Out of the storehouse of mythology, Bacon selects thirty-one fables and draws from them lessons to illuminate not only the true nature of science but also the moral and political conditions which must be fulfilled if science is to flourish and do good. He was well aware that "the mechanical arts may be turned either way, and serve either for the cure or for the hurt." This lesson he discovers in the fable of Daedalus, whose ingenuity was applied now to good, now to evil, ends and resulted finally in the death of his own son.

Then there are those who neglect the deeper truths of science in their anxiety to snatch at immediate profitable applications. Atalanta, who lost the race because she stopped to pick up the golden apples, symbolizes this failing. The futility and wickedness of religious wars and persecutions Bacon illustrates by the story of the Homeric hero Diomede, who at the prompting of Minerva, goddess of wisdom, fought and wounded Venus, goddess of love. He is the type of the religious zealot, confident in the wisdom of his cause and the worthlessness of the enemy, but unable to discern the folly of his violence. In the end, Diomede lost his life and ruined his cause.

Again Bacon sought for an active philosophy which would force nature to reveal her secrets. The justification for this he finds in the story of Proteus, the old god of the sea, who knew all the answers but would disclose none, until caught and held fast. Then, under constraint, he wriggled and twisted and turned himself into every shape—fire, water, or some wild beast—but in the end came back to his own form and told the truth.

Thus Daedalus stands for the scientific genius who can solve practical questions but lacks moral vision. Atalanta stands for the man who brings to science only the itch for profit, not the patience to win the highest prize of truth.

Diomede is the religious zealot, who creates a spiritual climate in which religion itself is the final victim. Proteus is the universal matter of nature, whose manifold transformations under the pressure of experiment it is the business of science to find out. And so for the other fables.

Truly, this was a subtle and brilliant book. At first sight it is no more than a contribution to the study of mythology made fashionable by Italian writers. But its real business was to plant in men's minds the vital ideas of a new age. It succeeded. It was immediately popular in Latin, in English, and in other modern tongues.

12

The Tide Turns

The Wisdom of the Ancients is the work of a man at the height of his genius. It seems also to be the product of a happy mind. More than one cause could account for this. So far as his philosophy is concerned, Bacon had come through a hard, lonely effort of thought; and even though he had decided against publishing a direct statement of his views, he had discovered in *The Wisdom of the Ancients* an indirect and inoffensive means of popularizing ideas which would bear fruit in good time.

His personal life also had assumed a more cheerful complexion. We have spoken often of his gift for friendship, but we have had nothing yet to record of love or marriage. And indeed women always played a subordinate part in his life. We have noted his affection for his mother, and we might have added his lively and undying gratitude to the wife of Sir Amyas Paulet, who had mothered him during his two-

and-a-half years as a very young man in Paris. But there is nothing romantic in these attachments.

His writings give us the same impression as his life. The essay on *Friendship* is notably full and warm. The essay on *Love* is quite forbidding. "The stage," it begins, "is more beholding to love than the life of man. For as to the stage, love is ever matter of comedies, and now and then of tragedies. But in life it doth much mischief, sometimes like a Siren, sometimes like a Fury." The essay on *Beauty* is more significant still. The brief treatment contains memorable things. "In beauty, that of favour is more than that of colour, and that of decent and gracious motion more than that of favour. That is the best part of beauty which a picture cannot express; no, nor the first sight of the life. There is no excellent beauty that hath not some strangeness in the proportion." Here there is great delicacy of perception, but the only examples given are beautiful men.

We shall not be wrong in concluding that Bacon cared more for his own sex than for women. We might even credit him with a fixed determination to remain a bachelor when we read in his explanation of the fable of Orpheus: "It is wisely added in the story, that Orpheus was averse from women and from marriage; for the sweets of marriage and the dearness of children commonly draw men away from performing great and lofty services to the commonwealth; being content to be perpetuated in their race and stock and not in their deeds."

However, the platonic ambition to perpetuate himself in his deeds and not in his children did not wholly satisfy Bacon. When he was about thirty-six he began to woo—or at least to get influential friends to forward his suit for—a young widow who was both beautiful and rich. He did not succeed. She married his rival Sir Edward Coke—an able but rancorous man, with whom Bacon found it difficult to maintain even the minimum of polite behavior without which life was unpleasant to him. If he had wanted to do Coke a bad turn he could not have done him a worse one: Lady Hatton (that was the widow's name) made him a thoroughly bad wife.

Congratulating himself, no doubt, on his escape, Bacon gave up the thought of marriage for some years, and then made a venture of a very different kind. Among his colleagues in the House of Commons was a London alderman named Benedict Barnham, who left four daughters when he died. The second was named Alice, and on her Bacon fixed his choice. In 1603, when he was forty-two and she still but a child, he told his cousin, Robert Cecil, that he "had found out an alderman's daughter, an handsome maiden to my liking." He waited three more years and then he married her. To us, it would not seem very romantic, but it was usual enough in those days. Francis was forty-five, Alice fourteen. "Sir Francis Bacon was married yesterday," writes a contemporary gossip, "to his young wench in Maribone Chapel. He was clad from top to toe in purple, and hath made himself and his wife such a store of fine raiments of cloth of silver and gold that it draws deep into her portion." The account rings true. Bacon always loved magnificence, and purple was a favorite color. No doubt he was happy in the prospect, and no doubt his life thereafter was happier than before. At least till near the end. At the very end he struck her out of his will for some grave fault, which is not specified, though he did not leave her unprovided for. The haste with which she married after his death suggests that she had tired of her old husband. There were no children of the marriage, nor have we any record of such companionship as the marriage of his father and mother provided.

About the time of his marriage, Bacon's political prospects

also began to improve. All his life he had done plenty of hard service for Elizabeth and James. At last the recognition came. In 1607, he became Solicitor General, in 1613, Attorney General, in 1617, Lord Keeper, in 1618, Lord Chancellor and Baron Verulam, in 1621, Viscount St. Alban.

He had climbed even higher than his father, and like his father he could now indulge his taste for building. The supply of piped water had given out at Gorhambury. Since the water would not come to his house, Baron Verulam moved his house to the water. Verulam House was in advance of the age for elegance and convenience. "The most ingeniously contrived little pile that ever I saw," wrote a contemporary— and well he might. It had its kitchen, larders, and cellars tucked away in the basement; it had Turkish baths and a roof garden. It had other extensive gardens also. The tastefulness of their layout will be clear to any one who cares to read his essay on the subject.

"And because the breath of flowers is far sweeter in the air, where it comes and goes like the warbling of music, than in the hand, therefore nothing is more fit for that delight than to know what be the flowers and plants that do best perfume the air. . . . That which above all others yields the sweetest smell in the air is the violet; specially the white-double-violet, which comes twice a year, about the middle of April and about Bartholomew-tide. Next to that is the musk-rose. Then the strawberry-leaves dying, which yield a most excellent cordial smell. . . . But those which perfume the air most delightfully, not passed by as the rest but being trodden upon and crushed are three: that is burnet, wild-thyme, and water-mints. Therefore you are to set whole allies of them, to have the pleasure when you walk or tread."

13

The New Atlantis

In Bacon's mind there was always some conflict between his duty to his country and his duty to mankind. He distinguished three grades of ambition. The first was merely personal ambition, which he dismissed as vulgar and degenerate. He allowed more dignity to those whose ambition was for their country, and of this he had his full share. "But," said he, "if a man endeavour to establish and extend the power and dominion of the human race itself over the universe, his ambition (if ambition it can be called) is without doubt both a more wholesome thing and a more noble than the other two."

Naturally, then, when Bacon became Solicitor General in 1607, he was not completely happy. The duties of his office piled up on his shoulders, and the haunting fear awoke that he was neglecting the highest ambition for one less noble. We happen to have the proof of this in a diary he kept for the

month of July, 1608. In it he jots down details of the mass
of public business to which he had to attend: it seems enough
to have absorbed the energies of three or four men. In the
midst of these notes comes a long section devoted to new
plans for promoting his philosophical reform.

From this it is clear that he was again thinking of making
a clean break with politics. He still wants "command of wits
and pens," but he has the idea that he could get this if he were
appointed head of some college. He thinks of Westminster,
Eton, Winchester as suitable places. Or Magdalen in Oxford,
or Saint John's in Cambridge, or, above all, of his own alma
mater, Trinity. He reminds himself to speak to the Archbishop and the Lord Treasurer about it. If he could get such
a headship he would turn the college over to scientific research. He plans the building, equipment, and staff that would
be wanted, and notes the need of money for travel and ex-
change of information with foreign centers of learning. He
jots down the names of scientists who might help, among
them Sir Walter Raleigh, then a prisoner in the Tower but
allowed facilities for research; he was said to have devised a
means of getting fresh water from salt by distillation. This
is just the sort of practical result Bacon wanted, though he
aimed most of all at fundamental research. He notes down
in his diary the desirability of rewards for successful inventors,
and of dismissing those who, after trial, are found to be incompetent. He also jots down names of men who might give
or bequeath money to his college, among them Lancelot
Andrewes, who is realistically described as being rich, sickly,
and a friend to experiments—three good reasons for expecting
help from him!

Bacon did not resign his office, but it was probably about
this time that he thought of a new way of stirring up interest

in his plan. He outlined a utopia in which the well-being of the inhabitants depended on their possessing such a scientific institute as he suggests in his diary. Thomas More's *Utopia* had exerted great influence on men's thoughts, but none on their actions; his proposals were not really practicable. Like Bacon, More had been deeply distressed at the growth of poverty, but he could suggest no better remedy than a more equal division of wealth, and was troubled in mind about the political disturbance that might follow any attempt to enforce it.

Bacon did not agree with More's ideas. Where there was not enough to go round, it did not help very much to suggest equal shares. He aimed instead at a great increase in the volume of wealth by the application of science to production. And there were other benefits also that science might bring, like improved health. It filled Bacon with indignation to find so many diseases described as incurable. This only meant, he said, that the doctors had so far failed to find a cure, not that a cure was impossible. It was with these thoughts in mind that he wrote his *New Atlantis*, giving it this title in reference to Plato's fable of an ancient submerged continent called Atlantis.

In Bacon's fable an English ship with fifty-one souls aboard is ploughing east from Peru. They have been long at sea and have many sick. They are delighted to sight land and are filled with hope and curiosity when a boat puts out to them bringing a document written in Hebrew, Greek, Latin, and Spanish, sealed with symbols which suggest that the inhabitants are Christians. For fear of infection, they are forbidden to land till visited by the Conservator of Health. When this official arrives, he carries a fruit in his hand the scent of which protects him. He arranges the manner of their coming ashore; and, when they offer him a present, he smiles and brushes them aside. "What, twice paid!" he exclaims, implying that he has an adequate salary from his government. The English sailors have plenty to surprise them—a public health officer, with a salary that makes him indifferent to a fee, and a remedy against infection.

Once ashore, the voyagers are billeted in the Strangers' House, "a fair and spacious house built of brick of somewhat a bluer colour than our brick." There are four single rooms for the ship's officers, fifteen double rooms for the crew, and seventeen separate cells in a long dormitory for the sick. When dinner was served, it turned out to be "better than any collegiate diet that I have known in Europe," the wine, ale, and cider being specially good. As for the invalids, they were fed on scarlet oranges and dosed with gray-white pills. The effect was wonderful. "They thought themselves cast into some divine pool of healing, they mended so kindly and so fast." The usual disease of sailors on long voyages in those days was scurvy, which is best treated by citrus fruits. It looks as if the utopians had anticipated one of the discoveries of later science.

In every encounter with their hosts, the strangers find evidence of their Christian beliefs and practice. The Governor of the Strangers' House is a Christian priest. When they inquire of him how, in their remote part of the world, they had come to be evangelized, they are told that a divinely guided ark had brought the Scriptures to their shores. Bacon, of course, in common with most of his fellow-countrymen of the reformed faith, based his religion upon the Bible and regarded the Church simply as the Ark in which it was kept safe.

They find also a small Jewish element in the population

who live on terms of mutual respect with the other inhabitants. From one of them they learn of a certain King Solomona who had ruled there nineteen hundred years before. In his reign was founded the scientific institute which was the real soul of the island. It was called Solomon's House, either in memory of Solomona or of the bibical King Solomon. Bacon preferred to look to the Hebrew rather than the Greek tradition for his deepest wisdom. The choice of the name Solomon's House instead of some Greek term like the Academy or the Lyceum, which would recall Plato or Aristotle, is deliberate. Deliberate also is the choice of the alternative title, the College of the Six Days' Works. Bacon means, of course, that the science of natural philosophy is nothing else but the study of God's works during the six days of the Creation. The islanders, as Bacon recommended to his fellow-countrymen, learn the will of God from the Bible, and the power of God from the study of the book of nature. The island, very fittingly, is called Bensalem, Son of Peace.

The culmination of the visit is a meeting with one of the Fathers of Solomon's House. He is described as "a man of middle stature and age, comely of person, and with an aspect as if he pitied men." The all-embracing purpose of their studies, the Father explains, is "the enlarging of the bounds of human empire to the effecting of all things possible." The equipment of the house, as we might guess, comprises a library, botanical and zoological gardens, parks, pools, a museum, and various still-houses or laboratories. Here the Fathers have made many great discoveries.

In the gardens they practice grafting and inoculating, and have found out how to make plants mature earlier or later than their natural seasons. The importance of this in an age when there were no refrigerators is obvious.

In the parks are birds and animals for experiment and cross-breeding. By their experiments they have made notable advances in medicine and surgery. By crossing they have produced larger and stronger breeds.

They have deep caves under high hills to assist investigation of nature's subterranean activities, and lofty towers on great mountains for the study of meteorological phenomena. They are able to imitate snow, hail, rain, thunder, and lightning.

They aim at drawing new foods out of substances not now in use; at making new threads for weaving and new materials, like paper and glass, as well as artificial minerals and cements. They have also engines for enforcing and multiplying motions of many sorts, and furnaces that produce a great variety of heats. They have improved telescopes, microscopes, and spectacles. They imitate the flight of birds, and have some degree of flying in the air. They have also ships and boats for going under water. Nor do they forget to praise and thank God daily for His marvelous works and to implore His aid and blessing for the illumination of their labors and the turning of them into good and holy uses.

Such is the *New Atlantis*. Again it is an unfinished piece, and was not published till after Bacon's death. What is missing is an account of the political institutions of Bensalem. This is much to be regretted. The industrial revolution, when it did come, was often turned to anything but good and holy uses. The genius of Bacon was as strong for politics as for science. At the present day, the pouring of capital into backward countries in order to promote their industrialization often fails. It is much easier to teach the technological know-how to the native technicians than to equip the government with the political institutions that would make industrialization beneficial to the whole population.

Very likely Bacon found this the harder part of his task and left it till too late. But we do know from his other writings that he recommends a state of society in which "wealth is dispersed in many hands, and not engrossed into a few; and those hands not much of the nobility, but most generally of inferior conditions," such as "merchants, burghers, tradesmen, freeholders, farmers in the country, and the like."

14

The Great Instauration

Bacon, we have said, became Lord Keeper in 1617 and Lord Chancellor in the following year. There is no essential difference between the offices. He became Keeper by the mere act of King James handing him the seals; he became Lord Chancellor when he received an official confirmation of his appointment in the form of a Letter Patent. The Lord Chancellor is always raised to the peerage, so Bacon had become Lord Verulam. He was now in official rank the highest civil subject in the land. When James went on a visit to Scotland, Bacon acted as regent. During the King's absence he was virtually king. So high did he climb before his fall.

As Keeper or Chancellor, his duty was to preside in the Court of Chancery; and here he administered that branch of the law known as Equity. The purpose of Equity is to correct the law when the rules work out unfairly in individual cases. As King James put it: "Where the rigour of law in many cases will undo a subject, then the chancery tempers the law with equity, and so mixes mercy with justice, as it preserves a man from destruction." Obviously this system leaves a lot to the discretion of the Chancellor. So much is this so that the famous lawyer and antiquary, Selden, who was a contemporary of Bacon and knew him well, says in his *Table Talk*: "Equity is according to the conscience of him that is chancellor, and as that is larger or narrower, so is equity."

When Bacon assumed this enormously responsible office he did two characteristic things. First he rode in triumph, dressed, as at his wedding, in a suit of purple satin, from Gray's Inn to Westminster Hall to open the Law Courts. He liked a bit of pageantry. Secondly, in his opening speech, he promised speedy justice. "Fresh justice is sweetest," he said. Then he at once applied himself with quite extraordinary energy to clearing off arrears of cases that had accumulated during the illness of his predecessor. There were literally thousands of cases demanding settlement. His friends told him he would work himself to death. "The duties of life are more than life," he commented, adding with dry humor, "and if I die now I shall die before the world be weary of me, which in our times is somewhat rare." At last the time came when he could announce: "This day I have made even with the business of the kingdom for common justice. Not one cause unheard." The job had been done in a few months. Such was his conscience, such was his dispatch. In the four years before his fall, he dealt with over seven thousand cases.

Nevertheless, even in the midst of such arduous routine, he kept room for the main purpose of his life. In the speech in which he promised speedy justice he confesses that he means to reserve the long vacations, or part of them, free for the studies to which in his nature he was most inclined. And so it came about that in 1620, two years after he became Chancellor, and as he was approaching sixty years of age, he had at last, if not finished, at least brought to a fit state for publication, his *Instauratio Magna*, (*The Great Instauration*). This had been his principal preoccupation ever since the day, some thirty-five years earlier, when he had put into circulation among his parliamentary friends his youthful essay with the boastful title of *The Greatest Birth of Time*. Even then he had been looking for office to help him with the work. Now at last he had attained to the highest office in the land; and with all the prestige of his Chancellorship to back him he could offer to the world so much of his project as his busy life had permitted him to perfect.

The book, which his secretary Rawley assures us he regarded as "the chiefest of his works," was dedicated to the King. "After my death," writes Bacon, "I may yet perhaps, through the kindling of this new light in the darkness of philosophy, be the means of making this age famous to posterity;" and he begs the King, "who resembles Solomon in so many things," to "follow his example in providing for the collecting and composition of a Natural and Experimental History . . . such as philosophy may be built upon." The dedication to the King is followed by a preface to the people, in which he entreats them to believe that the business in hand is "not an opinion to be held, but a work to be done." He is laboring, he says, "to lay the foundation, not of any sect or doctrine, but of human utility and power," and he calls upon his fellow-countrymen to join in the work.

Then in a section called "The Plan of the Work" he explains the relation of the present volume, *The Great Instauration*, to his project as a whole. The present volume is concerned with natural philosophy, but this does not cover the whole of knowledge. It is but one division, though an extremely important division, of the whole field. For an understanding of the whole field and the place of natural philosophy in it, he refers his readers to the already published *Advancement of Learning*, where religion, politics, ethics, law, history, and literature are given their due.

For the progress of natural philosophy the chief requisites are (1) a new kind of logic, which will offer not simply an analysis of nature but a key to the control of nature, and (2) a new kind of encyclopedia, which will include with a description of natural phenomena an account also of all the arts and crafts. The new logic he calls *The New Organon, or Directions concerning the Interpretation of Nature;* the new encyclopedia he calls *The Phenomena of the Universe, or a Natural and Experimental History for the Foundation of Philosophy*.

The completion of the whole endeavor he does not expect to live to see. "That is a thing both above my strength and beyond my expectation. What I have been able to do is to give it, as I hope, a not contemptible start. The destiny of the human race will supply the issue, and that issue will perhaps be such as men in the present state of their fortunes and of their understandings cannot easily grasp or measure. For what is at stake is not merely a mental satisfaction but the very reality of man's well-being, and all his power of action. Man is the helper and interpreter of nature. He can only act and understand in so far as by working upon her or observing her he has come to perceive her order. Beyond this he has neither knowledge nor power. For there is no strength that can break the causal chain: Nature cannot be conquered but by obeying her."

A profoundly new philosophy underlies this book, a new

way of regarding the relation between man and nature. Man is no longer simply the rational animal capable of understanding nature; he is the helper of nature, the cooperator with nature; and the proof of his understanding lies in his power to cooperate. The bond between man and nature is more intimate, more complex, than before. Nature is not something that lies outside man, which he can contemplate. That was the old view, and Bacon calls it by the picturesque name of *pastoral* philosophy. But nature, as Bacon saw, is something which man himself has in part made. He builds shelters, makes clothes, lights fires, tames rivers, encloses and tills fields, mines minerals, manufactures tools; and what he knows of nature is revealed to him in the course of these purposive activities. Man cannot escape this destiny. To live he must do more than contemplate nature, he must help her, he must cooperate.

Bacon confesses that, as he thought these new thoughts, he was not only aware of the shocks of hostile opinion and of the fogs and clouds of nature, but that he suffered private and inward hesitations and scruples. He was preaching a new doctrine of the nature and responsibilities of man, and it seemed fraught with danger as well as hope. He would teach man to grasp new powers; but seeing the villainies which abounded on every side, he might well tremble to think how men would use them.

But he fortified himself ultimately with religious beliefs that were as new as his doctrine of man. God, he argued, has created man in His own image; therefore man, in his lesser way, must also be a creator. That is why God promised Adam dominion. But dominion was promised on condition that he did the will of God, the prime obligation of which is obedience to the law of love. If man will again study the book of nature, with the firm resolve to govern the power he wins thereby in the spirit of charity, that will be the fresh start, the new beginning.

The greatest birth of time, the masculine birth of time, the New Atlantis, the great instauration—all were names for the same thing, namely, the sober resolution to make a fresh start, to wipe the slate clean of intellectual pride and selfish will; and in humility toward God, reverence toward His works, and charity toward men, apply himself with zeal to the task of lessening human wants and sufferings.

All the experience of the three hundred and fifty years since Bacon began to publish these thoughts show how right he was. Man can neither escape his role as the helper and interpreter of nature, nor make a sensible use of it, unless he empties his heart of selfishness. Such was the program Bacon drafted for the modern world.

15

Political Shipwreck

To become Lord Keeper and Lord Chancellor was a fulfill-
ment for Francis Bacon of more than one treasured hope.
He now held the office his father had held, the office playfully
conferred upon him by Elizabeth when he was a boy of ten;
and he held it in the spirit in which his father had held it, as
an opportunity for service. Witness the speed of his justice,
the clearing of the files, no suit left unheard.

The exalted office gave him also the opportunity, for which
he had waited all his life, to launch his program of reform
with a good hope that it would not fall unheeded from the
press. The long series of unfinished works, the carefully
finished but unpublished works—these now had their chance.
Into the first book of his *Novum Organum*, which is the
intellectual core of the whole great compilation, he packed
the substance of his published and unpublished writings in a
series of one hundred and thirty aphorisms which are the

ripest fruit of his genius. Written with consummate force, eloquence, and economy of words, in the international language of scholarship, it spread his influence swiftly into every center of culture in Europe and, after some delay, beyond. Bodley's criticism, that there could not be found a responsible body of academic opinion that would support his plea, soon looked absurd. Even the universities made some attempt to digest his thoughts, and where they failed, new institutions were created to put them into effect.

Of these institutions, the most famous is the Royal Society, founded in 1662, with acknowledgments to Francis Bacon as its chief inspiration. How well, on the whole, the founders understood his purpose is shown in a passage from the first history of the society. "Experimental science will overcome narrowness of mind; enable minds distracted by civil and religious differences to meet on neutral ground; and, in designing a union of men's hands and reasons, unite various classes and occupations." The pity is that King James, while Bacon was still alive, did not see fit to put in hand the work that was inaugurated thirty-seven years after his death by his grandson, Charles II.

But there was a third and more personal reason for Bacon to rejoice in his elevation. Now, as Lord Chancellor, he returned to his boyhood home at York House in the Strand, managing to secure a lease of it for twenty-one years from its current occupier, the Archbishop of York, who was Tobie Matthew's father. He celebrated his sixtieth birthday in his old home with a banquet at which the poet Ben Jonson proposed the toast in verse. Good verses, too, they are, with enough imagination and skill to fix for us the flavor of the moment of triumph.

Hail, happy Genius of this ancient pile!
How comes it all things so about thee smile?
The fire, the wine, the men! And in the midst
Thou stand'st as if some mystery thou did'st!
Pardon, I read it in thy face, the day
For whose returns, and many, all these pray;
And so do I. This is the sixtieth year
Since Bacon, and thy Lord, was born, and here;
Son to the grave, wise Keeper of the Seal,
Fame and foundation of the English weal.
What then his father was, that since is he,
Now with a title more to the degree;
England's high Chancellor: the destin'd heir,
In his soft cradle, to his father's chair:
Whose even thread the Fates spin round and full,
Out of their choicest and their whitest wool.

It was a peculiarity of Bacon's temperament that on the occasion of a piece of exceptional good fortune he often fell into an irrational depression of spirits. If he had done so a week after his birthday party when, in circumstances of special honor, he was created Viscount St. Alban, his low spirits would have been justified; for the plot that within a few weeks was to cast him from power was already in train.

In Bacon's day, the officers of the Crown had no adequate salaries. They lived on the fees and presents they received from those who had occasion to employ their services. The fixed regular salary might be as little as 5 per cent of the estimated value of the post. Bacon did not approve of this system. In his ideal commonwealth of Bensalem, it will be remembered, an official who is offered a present rejects it in surprise. But this was the system into which Bacon was born. He could not of himself abolish it, though he shared the opinion of the growing number of those who thought that what had once been a sensible way of doing things had now become an abuse. A movement was on foot to put an end to the system. Committees were set up in the House of Commons to inquire into monopolies—that is, grants by the Crown of exclusive rights to trade in certain articles—and also into abuses in the law courts. The two were not unconnected, for a decision in a court of law might defend a right to a monopoly. Bacon had no reason to feel disturbed. He did not approve of monopolies save under strict limitations, which it is easy to defend. He thought, for instance, that a man who made an invention might be protected in the sale of it for a certain time. As for the administration of his court, he knew, he said, that he had clean hands and a clean heart and need fear no man.

All the same, he had enemies who were determined to bring him down, and among the thousands of litigants who had appeared before him they found about a score who could be induced to put their name to a charge. Bacon could not deny, did not seek to deny, and had no reason to deny, that on the conclusion of cases and the giving of judgment he had received presents. It was by the receipt of such presents that his immense establishment at York House with its clerks, secretaries, and servants of every sort was maintained.

There were a few cases, however, in which it appeared that presents had been made before judgment had been given, and such presents might justly be called bribes, especially if they had affected the decision. But Bacon denied that he had ever sold a judgment, nor after his dismissal was a single judgment he had given reversed. The utmost Bacon would concede was that his servants had taken presents while a case was pending, and that there had been negligence on his part in allowing such a thing to come to pass.

The matter never came to a trial. The Lords constituted themselves into a tribunal to collect evidence and pronounce judgment without hearing his defence. Bacon protested, but at this point, for reasons that will no doubt never be clear, the King intervened. In a private interview, he urged Bacon to offer no defence but to make his submission to the peers, and trust to him, James, to bring the whole matter to a fitting conclusion. Bacon made his submission in sufficiently humble terms to satisfy the King and the Lords, but he confessed only to carelessness, not to corruption. He was deprived of his office, fined £40,000, and sent to the Tower. But the King had him out of the Tower in two days and remitted the fine. Bacon retired to Gorhambury, and, like the philosopher he was, bethought him of other great patriots who had fallen into discredit for a time—a Cicero, a Seneca, a Demosthenes —and set himself to make the best use of his liberation from the political treadmill.

But it was no light blow, though it was generally understood that he had been what we call "framed." The biographer Aubrey, who lived near his period and personally knew many who had known him, records the verdict of informed opinion. This was that his servants had taken bribes, "but his Lordship always gave judgment *secundum aequum et bonum*," that is, fairly and honestly. "All that were great and good," says Aubrey again, "loved and honoured him." His friends stood by him. "My conceit of his person," wrote Ben Jonson, "was never increased towards him by his place or honours; but I have and do reverence him for the greatness that was only proper to himself, in that he seemed to me ever by his work one of the greatest of men and most worthy of admiration that hath been in many ages. In his adversity I ever prayed that God would give him strength, for greatness he could not want. Neither could I condole in a word or syllable for him, as knowing no accident could do harm to virtue, but rather help to make it manifest."

But how did Bacon estimate himself? Advisedly and after reflection, in the consciousness of his personal integrity, he wrote: "I was the justest judge that was in England these fifty years." He speaks in round numbers, not wishing to go farther back lest he should claim to be a better man than his father. Then he adds, passing judgment on the whole system of remunerating judges by fees and presents: "It was the justest censure there was in Parliament these two hundred years," meaning that reform of the judicature was long overdue and that he welcomed it. Not that the reform began at once, if we may judge by the corrupt and incompetent wretch who slipped into the seat from which he had helped to dislodge Bacon.

16

The Harvest of the Last
Five Years

Bacon, at the urging of the King, had made a formal confession to the charge of corruption, but, in replying one by one to the particulars charged against him, he admitted no instance of corruption, and, when he concluded with the terse observation "I confess it was a great fault of neglect in me, that I looked not better to my servants," the effect was one of irony. He even made clear that the neglect was limited to the first two years of the four during which he had held the office, and we know that those were the years in which he was devoting the law terms to clearing off the accumulated arrears of business and his vacations to the composition of *The Great Instauration*. It was carelessness, not corruption, that had robbed him of the power to give speedy justice to his countrymen and a sounder philosophy to all mankind—two objects on which his heart was set.

The consciousness of his innocence and the magnitude of the concession he had made to the King, in offering a submission to the Lords instead of insisting on a trial, explain the tone of the letter he addressed to the King's favorite, the

Marquis of Buckingham, after his removal to the Tower: "Good my Lord, Procure the warrant for my discharge this day. . . . I was a true and perfect servant to my master, and one that was never author of any immoderate, no, nor unsafe, no (I will say it) nor unfortunate counsel; and one that no temptation could ever make other than a trusty, and honest, and thrice loving friend to your Lordship; and, howsoever I acknowledge the sentence just, and for reformation fit, the justest Chancellor that hath been in the five changes since Sir Nicholas Bacon's time."

Buckingham felt the justice of the protest and got him out at once. Bacon wrote, "My very good Lord, I heartily thank your Lordship for getting me out of prison, and now my body is out, my mind nevertheless will be still in prison, till I may be on my feet to do his Majesty and your Lordship faithful service." Bacon had five years left to live. In this chapter, we shall consider the use he made of them.

His situation, for the literary and philosophical labors he had in mind, was not wholly bad. He had lost his home in York House, but he could retire to Verulam. He had lost most of his wealth but not the loyalty of his friends, and they were the pick of the land. One of his first and greatest tasks was to expand the *Advancement of Learning* and turn it into Latin, the universal language. This had become urgent because that work had been incorporated into the plan of *The Great Instauration*, of which it now formed the first part.

The *Advancement*, hastily put together and published in 1605, consisted then of two books. The first was devoted to the praise of learning, and that needed no expansion. But the second attempted to sketch a map of the whole field of learning, with indications of notable deficiencies. This second book was now expanded into eight, and the whole work, now in nine books, came out in Latin, in 1623, under the title *De*

Augmentis Scientiarum. The expansion of the contents was, of course, entirely Bacon's work, but, in the translation of the work into Latin, he was glad to have the assistance of a number of secretaries. It is here that his friends proved especially useful to him.

Three were men of great fame in their own right. The first was Ben Jonson, the playwright, of whose intimacy with Bacon we have already spoken. The second, whom Bacon found the quickest and most efficient of the three, was none other than Thomas Hobbes, the future author of *Leviathan*, a book about the state, which has put him in the first rank of political philosophers. A man of acute and varied intelligence, he was yet of an arid nature compared with the richness and exuberance of Bacon. He settled the problem of the uniformity of religion by the simple expedient of insisting that the religion of any state should be laid down by the prince and accepted by the people as part of the obedience they owed their sovereign. Such a solution was wholly alien to the temper of Bacon, for whom religion was a personal experience, a deeply felt and conscientiously pondered response of the individual to the problem of the universe. The relationship between the two men lacked an essential element of warmth but rested on a mutual admiration for their intellectual powers.

The third secretary was closest to the mind and heart of Bacon and was possibly the rarest spirit of the three. This was George Herbert, younger brother of Lord Herbert of Cherbury, and now a gentleman of about thirty years of age, exquisitely equipped with the knowledge of ancient and modern tongues, the public orator of the university of Cambridge, and still intent on winning a career in the diplomatic service. But he also carried in himself the seed of a remarkable flowering of the spirit, which blossomed a few years after Bacon's death, when, as rector of Bemerton, near Salisbury, he wrote his prose masterpiece, *The Country Parson*, and the small volume of poems *The Temple*, which, on his deathbed, he entrusted to a friend to publish. That volume was to give him a unique place among Anglican poets and the claim, admitted by discerning critics, to inclusion among the major poets in the English tongue. When *The Great Instauration* was published, George Herbert, who saw in it a significance that many have failed to see, hailed the author (in a Latin poem) as the "alone-only priest of nature and men's souls."

The two men shared a fundamental sympathy in religion, and, when Bacon, during the enforced idleness of a severe illness, in 1624, translated a few favorite Psalms into English verse, he published the little volume with a dedication to George Herbert. He had no inkling then, I fancy, how great a poet Herbert was to prove. Bacon's own verses have only the merit of strong sense and deep feeling but no subtlety of rhythm or magic of phrase, no poetic individuality. As a maker of verses, he was on his father's level, an amateur with good sense and an undistinguished style.

Such, then, were the friends Bacon had about him to assist him in putting into a language all Europe could read a book that provides the general cultural background for his specific philosophical reform. To them should be added, to round off the circle of his friends, Bishop Lancelot Andrewes. To him, subscribing himself "Your lordship's loving friend," he dedicated in 1622 his fragment *Advertisement Touching a Holy War*, choosing Andrewes, as he wrote, "in respect of our ancient and private acquaintance, and because amongst the men of our times I hold you in special reverence."

Some critics complain that the insistence of Bacon on the importance of the mechanical arts has operated to lower the spiritual level of the modern world. One sometimes wonders whether these critics have read him. Bacon never taught that the progress of the mechanical arts was necessarily a blessing, only that it might be. "Certainly," he wrote, "human life is much indebted to them. The externals of religion, the adornment of cities, the culture of life in general, draw upon their store. But from the same source come instruments of lust and instruments of death, and well we know how far the subtle poisons, the engines of war, and other means of destruction, which are the product of mechanical invention, exceed the fabulous cruelty of the Minotaur."

The lesson of the *De Augmentis*, a great and rich work that profoundly influenced the life of Europe, is that the wise control of the mechanical arts can spring only from sound religion, wise politics, and a vigorous cultural life. Religion must, says Bacon, emerge from the cloister and permeate everyday life. States must rest upon the consent of the governed. The tradition of culture must be maintained.

"Without this tradition the history of the world," he writes, "seems to me as the statue of Polyphemus with the eye left out—that very feature which most marks the spirit and life of the person."

The creativity of the arts is the theme of a notably eloquent paragraph:

"As the sensible world is inferior in dignity to the rational soul, poetry seems to bestow upon human nature those things which history denies it. A sound argument may be drawn from poetry to show that there is agreeable to the spirit of man a more ample greatness, a more perfect order, and a more beautiful variety than it can anywhere (since the Fall) find in nature. So that this poetry conduces not only to delight but also to magnanimity and morality. Whence it may fairly be thought to partake somewhat of a divine nature; because it raises the mind and carries it aloft, accommodating the shows of things to the desires of the mind, not (like reason and history) buckling and bowing the mind to the nature of things."

If Bacon had published no more in his retirement than the *De Augmentis*, it would have been a heroic achievement for the tired and discarded statesman, but, in fact, it was only a fraction of what he actually accomplished. Already in the previous year he had published his *History of the Reign of Henry VII*. This, the first historical masterpiece in the English tongue, was written with almost incredible speed in the months immediately following his overthrow. He was released from the Tower at the beginning of June, 1621, and was able to retire to Gorhambury toward the end of the month. Four months later, the history was finished. It was published the following year.

Part of the explanation of the speed of composition, and also of the consummate excellence of the work, is that it was the result of prolonged meditation that he had previously lacked time to put into literary shape. The germ of it originated in his mind at about the time of the death of Elizabeth and the accession of James. Already in 1605, in the *Advancement*, he had outlined the theme. There, in deploring the inadequacy of existing histories, he pointed to the advantage of beginning with the well-defined and all-important period between "the uniting of the Roses and the uniting of the Crowns." He saw in this period the transition from a medieval to a modern kingdom, and the beginning of England's greatness as a world power.

To this period Henry VII was the key. His genius matched the period. The book is a political biography as well as a history, a penetrating portrait never since superseded of "one of the most sufficient kings" distinguished by possession of the "wisdom of the pilot." What a wealth can be found in it—

the extensive new legislation, the concern for peace, the economic growth (trade, manufactures, handicrafts, enclosures), the character of the population, the army, the navy, the thumbnail sketches of countless individuals, the tragicomedy of the two impostors who appeared during the reign. To discuss it adequately would require a book, not a paragraph.

But the supreme labor of Bacon's last years still remains to be mentioned. He had often proclaimed his belief that, without the new kind of *Encyclopedia* or *Natural and Experimental History*, which he had described in *The Great Instauration*, his whole philosophical scheme would have to be abandoned. It was for the compilation of this work that he had long sought the backing of the King and the command of wits and pens; now, there was no alternative but to attempt the task by himself. The seventh book of the *De Augmentis* deals with a famous topic of Baconian morality, the necessity to subordinate the claims of the individual to the common good. Here, in a passage addressed to the King, Bacon speaks of his own personal effort to conform with this law. "For myself, most excellent king, I may truly say that both in this present work and in those I intend to publish hereafter, I often advisedly and deliberately throw aside the dignity of my name and wit (if such thing be) in my endeavour to advance human interests; and being one that should properly perhaps be an architect in philosophy and the sciences, I turn common labourer, hodman, anything that is wanted; taking upon myself the burden and execution of many things which must needs be done, and which others through an inborn pride shrink from and decline."

What he was attempting to do was to publish monthly parts of a scientific work devoted to particular topics, of which he finished three—the *History of the Winds*, the

History of Life and Death, the *History of Dense and Rare*—
and to gather together, so far as he could, under the title of
Silva Silvarum, a great miscellany of information to serve
as an indication of what the desired encyclopedia should be
like. The desk work was exhausting, and he was also attemp-
ing, not with any outstanding aptitude for such research, to
carry out experiments in various fields.

It was thus that, one bitter day, toward the end of March,
1626, he stepped out of his coach into the snow on Highgate
Hill to buy a chicken from a cottage woman and try an experiment in refrigeration by stuffing it with snow. Seized with
a chill, he had himself carried to a friend's house in the neigh-
borhood, where he died on the morning of Easter Sunday,
April 9. From his sickbed, he wrote a cheerful letter to his
absent host, comparing himself, but without any apparent
thought that his own death was so close, to the old Roman
encyclopedist Pliny, for whom "as his predecessor" he had a
profound admiration. "My very good Lord," runs this last
of Bacon's letters, "I was likely to have had the fortune of
Caius Plinius the elder, who lost his life by an experiment
about the burning of the mountain Vesuvius." He was mis-
taken in thinking he was recovering, but it was a death such
as he desired, won in the eager pursuit of a noble end.

How are we now to estimate the influence of this man?
His name is known throughout the world; his thought is
studied everywhere and often better understood by foreigners
than by Englishmen. As a world figure, for what does he
stand? In the short study we have been able to make of him,
we have found that, though his roots were deep in his own
soil, his first thought was for the human race as a whole,
and the lesson he wished to teach mankind was its moral
obligation to exploit the inexhaustible wealth of nature and
to use this wealth in charity for the common good of all men.

Index